THE MUSIC DIET

The rock and roll route to a healthier, longer life

DR JULIA JONES

THE MUSIC DIET

THE MUSIC DIET

CONTENTS

Introduction   Page 9

1   Let's Get Physical   Page 13
     A brief history of our quest to stay healthy
     (and why we're failing)

2   Light My Fire   Page 34
     The effects of music listening on the brain

3   Let Me Entertain You   Page 54
     The health effects of performing music

4   Let's Dance   Page 77
     The physical effects of moving to music

5   Relax   Page 94
     The role of music in rest and sleep

6   Good Times   Page 116
     The social impact of music as we age

7   Stairway To Heaven   Page 132
     The importance of music in later life

8   The Scientist   Page 148
     The future of music and health research

9   Come Together   Page 161
     Joining the dots to harness the full 360° value of
     music in society

Listen to the playlist featuring the above songs at
www.musicdiet.co.uk

ACKNOWLEDGEMENTS

My huge gratitude to all of the many family members, friends and colleagues along the way who helped make this book idea a reality. Thank you. Extra special thanks to Rachel, mum, Sassy, Mark, Rufus, Charlie and the Devonshire Meirkats. I hope you enjoy the read.

THE MUSIC DIET

INTRODUCTION

"Music is part of being human. Music can lift us out of depression or move us to tears – it is a remedy, a tonic, orange juice for the ear."

Professor Oliver Sacks

I've written this book to show how you can use the science behind music's effect on the body and brain to live healthier for longer.

Drawing on research from around the world, including my own academic and professional work, we'll delve into how music delivers many benefits. For example, how it improves brain function, encourages and enhances physical activity and social engagement, can stave off degenerative illnesses associated with ageing and deliver many other positive results. You'll see how easy it is to incorporate music into your life and business for the mental and physical wellbeing of you, your family and your colleagues.

Music is all around us. In stores, in the car, in our homes, in restaurants, in films, on television, in our gyms, on our radios, in our earphones. Pop and rock music has deep emotional resonance with the three generations who have now grown up with it. But still it's largely overlooked by society, the medical world and businesses, despite its potential as a valuable asset. Professional sports men and women have already recognised the power of music and have been embedding it firmly in their training for many years. But they remain the exception and not the norm.

Popular music has long been the universal language of the mass population in the western world. It's the antidote to many of the growing problems we're facing today, especially in terms of health and wellbeing. The rise in obesity and diabetes is now a serious concern and traditional exercise campaigns and gym membership promotions are not working. Health and fitness industry revenues continue to rise but have failed to produce a healthy society. It's time to radically rethink our approach to health and recognise how music can help us achieve better results because as humans we are genetically drawn to it. A combined music and health club for example would be a much more enjoyable place to frequent than the usual fitness environment. It would help deliver social and mental health as well as physical health.

It's time to join the dots and harness the 360^0 value that music can deliver. From early education to end-of-life care and everywhere in between, there are multiple economic and health benefits that music can deliver in societies if properly harnessed and delivered.

My work over the past 25 years has focused on the effects of music on human behaviour. I've been prescribing music as an asset since the 1990s, helping individuals and businesses use it to stay alive and stay ahead. Since I started my professional journey I've witnessed first-hand how music successfully influences human behaviour. I've always used music strategically in my work as a DJ; a musician; a sports coach and personal trainer; as a lecturer public speaker; and a business consultant. The principles we'll explore in this book are scientifically proven and they work.

My first exposure to music's effect on cognitive psychology and neuroscience was while studying for my Masters in Sport and Exercise Psychology. I later took these same principles and applied them to clients ranging from Olympic squads to the general public. Now I use these approaches to help brands, businesses, cities, governments and organisations understand how music can positively affect their customers, their workforces, and their populations. We are now living in a world where experience has become more valuable than ever. The business vocabulary has become full of Xs – CX, EX, UX, IX. In late 2018 my company decided to throw a new X into the conversation and announced – MX – calling for professionals to properly embed Music Experience in their Customer Experience, Employee Experience, User Experience and Interactive Experience work.

In 2018 I was invited to present the core principles of the value of music in society at the United Nations' *World Urban Forum* in Kuala Lumpur, showing how music can help urban communities successfully deliver the UN's sustainable development goals. The world is waking up to the power of music. Don't get left behind. Throughout this book I've added tips and recommendations to help you easily identify ways that you can add more music into your daily life and workplace.

The first chapter explores our long fascination with "keep fit" and why the health and fitness industry to date has not managed to produce a healthy population. The rest of the chapters then go on to explain all of the many ways that music could help deliver health results and happier lives.

Think of *The Music Diet* as an 'all you can eat buffet'. Start feasting on it. Get more music in your life and in your business every day. You'll see immediate results. Music can make life better. This is the one diet you will happily stay on for life.

Julia Jones

1. LET'S GET PHYSICAL
*A brief history of our quest to stay healthy
(and why we are failing)*

Since the latter half of the 20th century there's been explosive growth in the fitness industry as it became intertwined with popular culture. The 1970s and 80s cultivated fitness icons such as Jane Fonda and Richard Simmons in the USA; The Green Goddess and Mr Motivator in the UK; exercise classes; health clubs and gyms; personal trainers; fitness fashion. Today the private health club market is worth over £3bn in the UK according to Mintel. The total market value of the UK health and fitness industry is almost £5bn according to year-end figures to March 2018 as compiled by the annual UK State of the Fitness Industry Report. Despite the fact that there are now over 7,000 gyms in the UK the penetration rate remains at just 14.9%.

For the past 6 years the market value of the UK health and fitness industry has achieved growth. Global figures show the same success according to the annual report by The International Health, Racquet and Sportsclub Association. Worldwide health club industry revenue reached $87.2bn in 2017. The USA leads the field with $30bn of revenues, far ahead of its closest rivals Germany ($5.6bn) and the UK ($5.5bn).

But obesity levels are continuing to grow too.

In this chapter we'll examine the growth of the health and fitness industry and the role that music has played in this boom. We'll examine some of the reasons why, several decades later, we're not reaping the long-term rewards of the gym culture and don't have a healthier society.

A potted history of fitness culture

The Greeks were famous for their love of fitness. In fact the word gymnasium stemmed from the Greek word "gymnos' which actually translates to naked. These gymnastic pursuits were solely directed at men and were intended to keep the population at peak fitness for competition or battle. Fitness alongside arts and education were the pillars of ancient greek philosophy. Early exercises even included hula hooping, an exercise that gained mass popularity in the 1950s and is still practiced by Grace Jones on stage at festivals around the world today. The original Olympic Games were staged in Olympia from 776 BC to 393 AD and provided the ultimate stage for competition. The games originated as part of a religious festival honouring Zeus, king of the gods. They were a true spectacle with performances and opening ceremonies as well as the sporting contests, described as "Woodstock" by Tony Perrotet, author of The Naked Olympics: The True Story of the Ancient Games. The ideal human body was literally set in stone and visible in the many sculptures and paintings that artists in this period left us. Music was present and respected but not yet woven tightly into exercise culture.

The Romans shared the ancient Greeks' interest in physical fitness and introduced baths as places for exercise and socialising. By the 15th and 16th centuries artists such as Da Vinci were still fascinated by the human form and physiology. In the 18th century a 'German Gymnasium' school was opened by Johann Basedow in Dessau. Dancing is thought to have been one of the activities included in the timetable. Soon afterwards Johann Christoph Friedrich Guts Muth (now considered the grandfather of gymnastics) introduced physical exercise into his school curriculum in Germany. He published the first coursebook for gymnastics featuring 29 different exercises. The book titled 'Gymnastics for Youth' included dancing. Friedrich Ludwig Jahn is considered the father of gymnastics and another teacher. His ambition was to use exercise to boost morale in his countrymen and military colleagues. Jahn launched the first open air gymnasium in Berlin in 1811 and the ideas spread rapidly. The gym was closed and Jahn was arrested in 1819 when authorities believed that his clubs were spreading political ideas. He was imprisoned until 1824 and then forbidden to live within 10 miles of Berlin. He is considered the pioneer of the parallel bars, rings and high bar. Similar principles appeared in other countries as the Highland Games in Scotland and athletics clubs in England started to adopt these ideals in the 1800s.

In 1847 Hippolyte Triat opened what is thought to be the first commercial gym. It was a huge centre in Paris, used by young men and the middle classes in pursuit of physical fitness. Triat was orphaned as a child and taken in by gypsies. He spent his youth performing as a strongman in their shows. Triat used his skills as an entertainer and performer in his exercise classes. He soon realised that his group classes were becoming very popular. In fact spectators used to come along and watch him train his participants. He is credited as being one of the first to introduce barbells into his exercise routines.

Inspired by Triat, Edmond Desbonnet, a French academic and photographer, opened a chain of commercial fitness centres in France. He also published regular physical fitness journals and books that helped to make fitness fashionable. He is often referred to as the 'Father of Modern Weightlifting'

The ideal physique was still very much based on muscular strength at this time and the fitness revolution was being led by and for men. By the mid 19th century fitness culture was embedded into life and education in most civilised societies. Males and females even started exercising in the same gymnasiums, something considered pretty radical back then. At the turn of the 20th century the idea of health and fitness was sweeping across nations. The gymnasium based, callisthenic style exercise routines were being replaced by apparatus designed to build strength and change body shape. There are some incredible photographs of gyms on board ocean liners including The Titanic, with men and women sitting astride exercise bikes cycling in full formal day wear. An 'electric horse' machine replicating riding motions also seemed popular at this time as it appeared in several gyms. Punch bags, parallel bars, and dumb-bells also appear in most photographs. Machines such as vibrating exercise belts and passive exercise tables also began to appear.

Fitness stars began to emerge in the early 1920s. Pioneers such as Charles Atlas marketed their own brand of health, fitness and bodybuilding courses and products. The ideal body - toned and muscular - became something to pursue. It was showcased on TV and in movies, with athletes such as Johnny Weissmuller in the Tarzan role during the 1930s. This movement grew rapidly in the 1950s and 60s when mainstream media increased the size of audiences. Jack LaLanne was one of the founders of the modern fitness industry. His national TV show, *The Jack LaLanne Show*, hit the screens in the USA in 1959, making him a household name. He opened a string of gyms, launched health and fitness products and continued his television show until the mid 1980s. He began bodybuilding as a teenager after hearing a talk about nutrition. He describes himself as a miserable and angry child due to his addiction to sugar and junk food. He turned his life around thanks to a change in his diet and exercise regime. He continued his daily exercise routine until his death aged 96. Female stars also started to emerge during the

1950s and 1960s. Bonnie Pruden and Debbie Drake were also given their own television shows in the USA, turning them into popular celebrities and fitness gurus.

The 1970s to the 2000s

By the 1970s fitness was mainstream as Hollywood stars such as Jane Fonda spearheaded health campaigns and Arnold Schwarzenegger championed the benefits of bodybuilding. Richard Simmons was also becoming a huge star. Music was becoming firmly embedded in this new culture and appeared influential in driving growth. Workouts were beginning to seem 'cooler' and more glamorous and appealing than before. Working out became a fashion statement and part of popular culture. Workout videos popularised aerobic exercise at home in the 1980s, fuelled by the affordability of home VHS and Betamax video players. Exercise aids such as The Thighmaster and the Bullworker reached great popularity as home exercise tools.

Among the workout videos one woman was top of the pops. Jane Fonda broke new ground, using songs during exercises to shape a specific journey that helped the overall delivery of the routine. It gripped a nation. Even the soundtrack became a highly popular compilation album in its own right. Featuring tracks such as *Can You Feel It* by The Jacksons, *Harbor Lights* by Boz Scaggs and *Bridge Over Troubled Water* by Linda Clifford, it reached number 7 on the UK Top 40 Chart.

Fonda (now aged 80) is still slim, flexible, funny and full of life. Fonda's original workout series released on VHS in 1982 became the highest selling video tape of all time, selling millions. In its first year it sold over 200,000 copies, leaving the blockbuster movies of the year trailing behind (*Star Trek II* and *An Officer And A Gentleman*). Her workout has since been re-released on DVD and continues to sell. I met Jane in 2017 and asked about her early music experiences. She recounted how her father, screen legend Henry Fonda, wasn't keen on her attending gigs so her early listening was largely based on his record collection, such as Nat King Cole.

Fonda still maintains her belief that exercise is essential to life. "I believe in fitness. Whether you're young, whether you're old, whether you've been exercising or just starting. It's important. It's maybe the most important thing in having a successful, long life." She also avoids sugar and carbs but says she's not obsessive about it. Some critics will point to her plastic surgery for this youthful look, but no-one can deny the main ingredient has been her lifetime of moderate exercise and healthy eating. My former health and fitness colleagues now aged 50+ also still look and feel great. It's no coincidence.

"Aerobics" wasn't the only form of exercise to music that was popular in the 1980s. The dance movie *Flashdance* became one of the most successful films of the era and still holds a cult following 30 years on. Television series *Fame* also became an award winning hit show between 1982 and 1987 and turned its male and female cast into huge stars both in the USA and overseas. The popularity led to a string of hit records and live tours. Fans around the world tuned in each week to watch Lydia Grant and Mr. Shorofsky teach students Leroy Johnson, Danny Amatullo, Coco Hernandez, Bruno Martelli and others new music and dance routines at the fictional New York City High School for Performing Arts. The theme songs of both *Flashdance* and *Fame*, performed by Irene Cara, became smash hits in the music charts. Legwarmers were a staple item in the female wardrobe. Tamara Rojo, a Royal Ballet principal ballerina, namechecked the impact of *Fame* in an interview in 2009. "*Fame* completely changed the look of dance. I was about 10 and studying ballet in Madrid. Until then we all wore pink leotards and tights. After we'd seen the TV show we started wearing black, ripping our tights and wearing t-shirts that were too big and falling off the shoulder. And legwarmers! We'd leave class saying we were just going to the corner shop for some water, but really we just wanted to be out on the street with our legwarmers."

Music, dance and athleticism was seemingly becoming the in-thing throughout the decade. In 1981 Olivia Newton-John enjoyed the biggest hit of her career when her single *Physical* held the Number 1 spot on the Billboard charts for 10 weeks and became the biggest selling single of 1982. Her music video perfectly harnessed the newly emerging opportunity that music television offered, and capitalised on the surge in popularity of exercise classes. Newton-John, playing the part of a headband-sporting exercise instructor, celebrated physical fitness with her band of superfit men. Then the out-of shape guys entered the scene and she got to work, helping them to achieve the perfect body. The video even gave a nod to gay fitness culture at the end of the video, although this part was often cut short on air by the conservative broadcasters of the era. Some even banned the video altogether. Everyone was jumping aboard the fitness wagon during the 1980s. Even the popular children's doll, Barbie, was in on the action with the release of "Great Shape Barbie" and her collection of fitness wear.

In the 1990s exercise to music classes continued to spawn a series of new styles and brands such as Zumba, Boxercise, Step Aerobics, Aqua Aerobics and Body Pump by Les Mills. These classes heavily involved the design of programmes that matched specific music beats and styles with particular physical movements. This choreography had already been seen in earlier decades but these more modern evolutions of exercise began to make much more purposeful use of music. In some cases the style of the music played a major role in creating the identity of the brand itself. Zumba, for example, very specifically aligned itself with latin inspired music and dance influences and quickly became popular with a wide age range of people, particularly women.

Sport and fitness wear crossed into mainstream fashion and music culture when leg warmers and headbands proved a hit. However, this reached new levels when Adidas found a new customer base after hip hop culture in the USA adopted its products in the 1980s and 1990s. Modern rap and hip hop acts such as Run DMC, Public Enemy, The Beastie Boys and N.W.A. all helped drive this style. The arrival of the Sony Walkman and the "ghettoblaster" made it possible to take your music with you.

Through the '80s, '90s and '00s these portable music devices evolved through many mutations as the technology continued to advance. Cassette Walkmans gave way to CD Walkmans, Mini-Disc Walkmans and eventually MP3 players. Music and exercise seemed to forge much closer ties during this period because the technology also enabled instructors to create their own playlists for exercise classes. It also made it much easier for individuals to listen to their own choices whilst exercising.

The 2010s

The 2010s witnessed a resurgence of a fitness trend that first bubbled up in the late 1980s and early 1990s. Group indoor cycling classes, also know as "spinning", re-emerged but this time with a much greater emphasis on music. It has now achieved a cult like following with many spin-off (excuse the pun!) brands such as Soul Cycle and Boom Cycle. These new brands place heavy emphasis on music. Indeed in many cases the fitness studio takes on a nightclub-esque vibe as the club classics boom out in the darkened space. This is all part of the experience.

The world has changed dramatically over the past century, especially for women. People of the 1910s would have been horrified at the sight of scantily lycra-clad men and women sweating while working out in public. It's become a normal part of our daily lives to see men and women working out, running, cycling, swimming, lifting weights. Music has become much more personalised. Individuals plug into their own music choices via their earphones. Now we're even able to access almost any song ever recorded thanks to our smartphones, fast download speeds, affordable mobile data bundles and streaming music services such as Spotify.

Music has certainly helped the fitness industry grow. But despite this growth our populations, especially in the western world, are getting fatter and less healthy. As I sat down to write this chapter, a well-timed announcement from Public Health England (PHE) revealed that 80% of over 40s in the UK are 'worryingly unhealthy'. Published just a few days after Christmas Day, it was no doubt designed to urge the population to make a renewed effort to get healthy in the New Year. It's a damning illustration of the failure of the fitness industry to keep the nation fit.

UK fitness industry revenues have continued to grow...
...but so have UK waistlines!

UK FITNESS
INDUSTRY
REVENUES

UK AVERAGE
WAISTLINE
SIZE

Local health and fitness establishments rub their hands

with glee each January as new recruits knock on their door. It's a business model that is well established. Step 1 – sign up new members to a monthly subscription in January. Step 2 – even though you don't see them again after a few months keep taking their money until they get around to cancelling their standing orders. I was heavily involved in this business model myself for almost a decade while managing a chain of health clubs in England throughout the 1990s.

The PHE results have been gathered from PHE's 'How Are You' quiz that has been completed by 1.1 million people so far. It's an impressive sample size. According to the official findings, 83% of 40 to 60 year olds in the UK (87% of men and 79% of women) are either overweight or obese, exceed the Chief Medical Officer's (CMO) alcohol guidelines or are physically inactive. This is pretty alarming when you view the current BMI (Body Mass Index) guidelines and see how broad the "Healthy Weight" range is. According to the National Center for Health Statistics (2017) almost 40% of adults and 19% of youths in the USA are obese. In the UK 26% of adults are obese. Modern life seems to be harming the nation but I would add that it may actually be modern attitudes that are predominantly the problem. Many people according to PHE can't actually identify what a 'healthy' body looks like, suggesting obesity has become the new normal. 77% of men and 63% of women in middle age are overweight or obese in the UK. Fashion brands now offer XXXXXXL sizes for men to cater for the fact that the average male waist has been rising in Britain and is currently just under 38 inches. Obesity in adults has hit an all time high. If we can't reverse this problem we're all in for a rocky ride ahead. The diabetes rate among this age group has also increased in England. Obese adults in the UK are more than 5 times more likely to develop Type 2 diabetes than those who are a healthy weight, according to PHE. According to the American Diabetes Association this problem is also rampant in the USA where the total cost of diagnosed diabetes was $327 billion in 2017. This relates to $237 billion for direct medical costs and $90 billion in reduced productivity. 60 million people in Europe also live with diabetes and, according to the World Health Organisation, diabetes deaths are likely to double by 2030. In an ageing society health services and the economy will struggle to cope with this issue in the coming decades.

But here's the dichotomy: on the same day that these figures make national news headlines in the UK there are more than 5 cookery shows on our main television channels, showing the population how to make dishes that are rather unhealthy. Shows such as *The Great British Bake Off* have taken the UK by storm and take primetime positions on mainstream terrestrial television. We've seen a steady stream of celebrity chefs explode into household names with their own TV shows, book ranges, restaurants and supermarket product ranges over the past two decades. Many of them use recipes that are laden with generous helpings of sugar and calories. Modern life is indeed causing problems, but a proportion of it is also perhaps potentially influenced by what we watch whilst sitting as couch potatoes after work each evening. Food programmes are now literally devoured by the general public and take primetime TV slots. The 'celebrity chef' has begun to reach rockstar proportions. To be fair some of these chefs have in more recent times moved towards healthier recipes, such as in shows by The Hairy Bikers and Tom Kerridge, who have all personally adopted healthier lifestyles. Hopefully this is a trend that will continue. The TV stars of previous decades were fitness gurus. The TV stars of today are chefs. These programmes attract significant viewing audiences so they have the potential to make a great health impact if they focus on healthy recipes.

Why do people find it so hard to get motivated to make the right decisions about health?

The PHE research blames 'the demands of modern life' for its alarming health statistic. Seemingly we are so busy with work and families that we no longer have time to use our common sense and ensure we follow a few very simple guidelines to look after our bodies. This statement may sound harsh but, if you are able bodied, it isn't difficult to use the stairs instead of the lift, or to buy vegetables instead of frozen meals. It's a choice. It's just that most of us choose not to do what we know we should be doing. These bad choices are usually not forced on us. So the problem isn't necessarily linked to the demands of modern life but more likely determined by our lack of willpower and our general inertia.

I've been a health and fitness professional for more than 20 years. In trying to help and encourage people to lose weight and make small but key changes to their lifestyles I've learnt that when dealing with humans, achieving these changes on a permanent basis is often easier said than done. I have to also keep reminding myself to stick to these principles in my own life! There's no doubt that it's a daily challenge. There has been some discussion regarding whether concepts such as nudge theory can automatically influence behavioural changes for healthier lifestyles. For example, putting healthy snacks at supermarket tills instead of sugary ones. These can certainly help make changes at the micro decision making level. But achieving or influencing significant behavioural changes on a larger scale is a complex challenge. In 2011 the *British Medical Journal* published an article examining whether 'nudges' are an effective public health strategy to tackle obesity. The conclusion was that the nudge approach "will be no substitute for regulation of the food and drinks industry, but it may nonetheless serve the social good". Simple incentives have not to date proved effective in motivating sustained weight loss. Governments are going to need to get tough. In 2018 some taxation measures on sugary drinks were introduced in the UK to try and implement these changes. 'Sin taxes' previously only linked to alcohol and cigarettes have in recent years been introduced in several countries to stem the consumption of unhealthy food. This is a government move that is likely to continue in order to stop people consuming so much unhealthy food and drink.

Getting people to move more often is the other side of the problem. Sport England data shows that encouraging participation is still a problem. In 2016 just 7.8 million people in the UK were doing 30 minutes of moderate exercise 3 times a week. With health experts now urging 30 minutes of exercise 5 times a week, we are still a long way off target. This data doesn't include recreational walking or cycling so our nation of dog lovers probably aren't included here. (My twice daily dog walks help me clock up approximately 10,000 steps a day). With inactivity and prolonged periods of sitting down now recognized as a greater threat than smoking encouraging participation amongst the general public is critical. The links between sedentary lifestyles and diabetes, obesity, cardiovascular disease and even certain cancers have been proven. We need to get people up and out of their chairs as often as possible every day. Perhaps the greatest opportunity in the history of health and fitness is the advances in technology that are now becoming part of our everyday lives. 85% of the UK population aged 16-75 years old now owns or has access to a smartphone. Apps can measure daily movement to help motivate users by giving reminders when they haven't moved for a while. I haven't yet found any data to determine whether they succeed in driving long-term behaviour changes.

Our unhealthy population hasn't emerged because the guidelines promoted by fitness gurus in past decades were wrong. It's because the nation didn't follow them. They ignored the advice and didn't adopt the lifestyle long-term. They fell off the wagon. That isn't to say that the health and fitness industries aren't also capable of making mistakes. A number of health recommendations today overturn some recommendations of previous eras. But let's consider the probable truth: most humans don't flock to exercise. Most fail despite their good intentions. This is even more difficult if your network of family, colleagues and friends don't also adopt the same healthy behaviour.

The fitness industry thrives on promoting an ongoing stream of 'get fit quick' solutions in magazines and adverts. All are aimed at pulling in customers who place more importance in changing the look of their bodies rather than their fitness levels. If magazines simply featured headlines saying 'Move More, Eat Healthy and Eat Less For Several Years To Lose That Excess Weight' they would soon be out of business. The industry exists because people are repeatedly lured into short-term fixes that don't result in long-term changes. It's a very profitable cycle.

The National Institute of Diabetes and Digestive and Kidney Diseases developed an online tool to help people understand how to reach and maintain ideal body weight. Inputting your height and weight enables the calculator to determine your Body Mass Index (BMI) and shows where you are on the healthy weight scale. This attempt to simplify the information and encourage the public to take responsibility is an important issue. The rise of the advanced fitness industry in previous years may have resulted in fostering a perception amongst the general public that it's necessary to have a complex training programme, an instructor and gym machines to achieve results. However, the mechanics are much simpler than that. Just move more, eat less and eat well over a lifetime. There is an energy imbalance that we need to address. Portion sizes have grown over the years, and we've been taught to clear our plates. So why have all of these health and fitness trends over previous decades failed to win over the general population and deliver a healthy nation? It's because humans are often not very good at motivating themselves. This is where music has a huge role to play because it's an undisputedly effective motivational tool. The scientific body of research confirming that fact is vast and we will look at some of it in later chapters. Music can help drive affordable interventions that deliver results. I've been using it with myself and my clients for decades. It works for all ages and all income levels. You don't have to spend a fortune on gym memberships. Poverty has been shown to have a significant impact on fitness levels. Dr. Jennifer Smith Maguire (in her book *Fit for Consumption: Sociology and the Business of Fitness*) examines the value that the fitness industry delivers to communities. She found that the majority of people – particularly lower socioeconomic classes – don't benefit from local fitness industry provisions. A lack of economic capital, and consumption preferences among this group make participation unlikely. She also noted that the private provision of fitness services in an area can sometimes lead to reduced public provision. Meaning even less affordable access.

Governments and local authorities that reshape their definition of health and wellbeing will reap rewards. Getting people to enter fitness centres and gyms often enough to see results has proven exceptionally difficult. Even exercise equipment that has been placed in parks, and is free for all to use, hasn't achieved sufficient results in public health. We need to try new approaches to health and I believe music is the key to this.

How music can help you exercise harder and for longer.

My research in 1998 examined the effects of music on exercise motivation. Synchronising music to exercise can enhance performance, especially by delaying the onset of perceived fatigue and so prolonging activity. I used cycling as the test exercise. Participants were required to cycle for as long as they could in one session. Then to cycle to background music in another session. Then cycle in time to the beat of the music in a third session. Synchronising to the beat consistently produced better results, enabling participants to keep cycling for longer. This same result has been witnessed by many subsequent research projects over the past 20 years. It is proven that music can successfully keep people motivated for longer and can act as a positive distraction which helps to delay the perceived onset of fatigue. Of course the music selection must be appropriate (music that acts as an irritation is less likely to be as effective) but in general, mainstream uptempo music can lift mood, distract from fatigue and boredom and improve results.

This music intervention can be highly effective for individual sessions, but in public exercise settings it often struggles to be effective - especially for those who need it most. Over the years I've often seen older women enter local gyms that feature loud, repetitive tracks selected by the young fitness staff. This isn't a match. In fact, it can be off-putting and extremely irritating. There is a vast difference between the member groups of local health clubs, ranging from young men intent on building muscle to retired women trying to manage weight or recover from illness or injury. Their music preferences are different. Gym staff are taught this but in practice it's often neglected. However, advances in modern gym equipment have enabled a more personalized approach, enabling users to plug their headphones into the machine to watch television or listen to music whilst cycling, for example. But watching daytime television doesn't produce the same motivational effects as upbeat music. Brands such as Nike continue to build music into their actual products and campaigns. Its Nike+ Running programme involves a partnership with music streaming service Spotify for a range of music playlists as well as access to its 30 million song library. The app provides a detailed record of exercise performance. Nike Pace Stations invite users to input their pace goal and musical preference. This data creates a personalised 100-song playlist designed to push the runner's pace. Events are also tapping into music with increasing numbers of marathons and other challenges incorporating music into the day through DJs or live music performances on stages along the route or at the finish line. Activity trackers such as Fitbit can sync music playlists via smartphones.

Zumba International is trying to push new boundaries with its use of music. Its new "STRONG by Zumba" brand has turned the traditional use of music for exercise on its head. Rather than choreographing exercise and dance moves to existing songs, these classes use music that has been specifically composed for the exercise routine. The first artist to compose bespoke music for this programme is Timbaland. Zumba International intends to target a new, younger audience through this music innovation. In 2016 £140bn was spent on health across the UK - more than 10 times the figure that was ploughed in 60 years ago (after adjusting for inflation).

Music has certainly played a key role in helping the health and fitness field grow as a commercial industry. Professionals realised that it could be harnessed to help design and market exercise experiences that are more enjoyable – and therefore more attractive. Music today is very firmly embedded in exercise experiences. However, despite the growth of the industry the population is still not getting healthier. The link between exercise and diet and good health have been publicly promoted for several decades. I don't believe that this is now an education problem any longer. It's a motivational problem. People are aware of what they should be doing but don't choose to adopt this lifestyle on a permanent basis.

In the following chapters I'll show how consuming music in a variety of ways can more effectively help you exercise more often (both physically and mentally) in order to deliver a more sustained and enjoyable health benefit.

2. Light My Fire
The effects of music listening on the brain

Music you love makes you feel happy, might get your foot tapping, or even get you up and dancing. But how does it do that?

Scientists have been studying the effects of music on the brain for decades. From brain scanners spotting instant neurological responses, to longer-term impacts that can be seen by the naked eye.

The brain's responses to music can deliver profound psychological effects and help manage anxiety, stress and cognitive disorders. There is also proof of the positive impact it can have on pain management, sleep disorders, dementia, Parkinson's Disease, brain development and more.

Without the need for any skills or knowledge almost every person with a healthy mind is equipped with the capability of enjoying music and the positive effects that it can produce.

But how does science say the brain responds to music? Let's find out.

I regularly work sitting in the lobby of *The Grand Hotel* on The Leas promenade in Folkestone on the south coast of England. I find it easy to focus here. It has a lovely relaxed vibe, especially in winter when the open fire in the reception is roaring. The creative juices flow. I concoct many 'grand ideas' here, some of which come to fruition and some just evaporate, replaced by new ideas. I even have a favourite seat here. It's an old cream Chesterfield corner sofa with a high back. From it, I can hear the pianist in the adjacent restaurant playing popular classical pieces on a grand piano for customers enjoying their afternoon teas.

I'm sitting in this comfy chair right now, and the last afternoon tea customer has drifted away, but the pianist is still playing. But it's different. She's shifted to popular hits from the 1980s. I notice the staff started whistling the tunes - the young lad behind the bar in his 20s, the gentleman behind the reception desk in his 60s, and the lady at the restaurant desk in her 40s or 50s. I can hear them all humming along to Phil Collins' *In The Air Tonight* under their breaths.

No-one else sitting in the lobby bar seems to have noticed this. The staff themselves haven't even noticed it. They're all engrossed in their tasks. The bartender is stocking shelves, the reception guy is tapping vigorously on his computer keyboard, the restaurant lady is busily cashing up the till. None of them are actively listening to the pianist but they've all started humming along quietly to the tune. For the next 40 minutes the pianist rolls out a non-stop repertoire of 1970s and 1980s pop rock hits. Just quietly, as background music. Everyone within earshot of this piano is subconsciously or consciously processing the sounds. The brain is reacting to the music, whether they are focusing attention on it or not. These processes are common to us all. No matter what the song or the style the brain processes the sounds the same way, but additional neuro-responses happen when we have a particular emotional connection or taste for the music that is processed.

We humans love to categorise things. Whether it's artistic styles, or literature, we love a genre. And music could have one of the most diverse array of categories of all the arts. From Baroque to breakbeat, witchstep to glitch, these categories throw up barriers between audiences. Whereas in reality it's all 'just music'. The brain processes it in the same way no matter what date or where it was recorded.

Examining the effects of music on human behaviour

I accidentally starting studying the use of music in mood and human behaviour in the late 1980s. I was a tennis coach, a DJ and in a local rock band. While waiting for my tennis clients to arrive I would play music on court while practicing my serve. I'd either play it from my car stereo if the car was close by, or using my battery powered "ghetto-blaster" on court. It soon became clear that when clients (of all ages) arrived while my music was playing on court, there was a different energy right from the beginning of the session. It created a different atmosphere.

In the late 1980s I was actively incorporating music into the sessions. I started using it in the warm ups, asking clients to synchronise their moves to the music where appropriate. I'd select songs to fit the tasks, either through the appropriate beats per minute (bpm) or the lyrical content. My tennis coaching business grew quickly. My sessions were fun and people learnt quickly. Even now I still use this same principle when delivering lectures to students or the general public – the music I play while audiences are streaming into the room sets the scene and can have a powerful impact on the success of the session.

This fuelled my fascination with music and human behaviour. I signed up to a Sport & Exercise Sciences degree in 1990 and a Masters degree in Sport and Exercise Sciences in 1998. My Honours degree thesis examined the effects of music on self-confidence and belief in Welsh tennis squads. My MSc thesis looked at the effects of music on exercise endurance.

For my Masters I studied participants who were not all high level athletes. The tests, as referred to in the previous chapter, examined the effects that synchronising movement to music had on exercise performance. Participants were required to cycle at a given speed until they reached fatigue and could no longer continue. Groups were asked to do this on 3 separate occasions. Once with no music at all, then with background music, and thirdly whilst synchronising their cycling with the beat of the music.

The preparation for these tests was extensive because it involved a long period of tests that examined music taste. I used the *Brunel Music Rating Inventory* created by my thesis supervisor, Dr Costas Karageorghis. It was imperative to rule out personal preferences to the music and find songs that participants would react to in a similar way.

The findings of the study clearly showed how the process of synchronising movement with music produced a positive effect and delayed the onset of fatigue in almost every case. The study was presented at the British Association of Sport and Exercise Sciences annual conference and published in the Journal of Sport Sciences in 2000. To emphasise that these effects do not only apply to athletes, Costas and I also demonstrated this experiment live on air for BBC Television's Pebble Mill, using participants from the audience.

By the late 1990s I was working alongside the Sport Science team on the Sport Psychology programme for the GB Swimming Association. In the lead up to the 2000 Sydney Olympic Games, we used music to manipulate the mood and performance of the UK's greatest young swimming talent. Helping the young swimmers to select music and teaching them techniques to control their mood in both training and competition. Effective control of anxiety, self-confidence and motivation can mean the difference between a medal and no medal. Music can help control mood and behaviour but it's a very individualised process. There isn't a song that works for everyone. For instance, Andy Murray has praised Ed Sheeran's *Thinking Out Loud* for its calming properties whereas gold medal winning British cyclist Laura Trott used the upbeat *No Surrender* by Bruce Springsteen . Twenty years since I began researching this field, music is now a fully embedded part of the professional sports training mix. Costas has gone on to develop an impressive body of work in the field of music and exercise and sports performance. His research has shown that music can lower a person's perception of effort. It can encourage positive thoughts and help distract your mind from feelings of fatigue such as a fast beating heart, burning lungs and muscles. According to his tests music can reduce the perception of effort in endurance exercise by as much as 10%. It can regulate mood due to the release of neurochemicals and lyrical content can help with inspirational imagery

How The Brain Responds To Music

The brain is hugely complex. It ranks alongside outer space and the planet's oceans as things that, despite our advanced intellect, humankind is still struggling to fully explore and map precisely. However, as medical technology becomes more technologically advanced, we've been able to study this extraordinary structure in more detail.

The arrival of magnetic resonance imaging (MRI) has enabled detailed real-time observations to be made. Images are taken milliseconds apart so we can see how the brain responds to a stimulus. We can even compare the resting state of the brain and the blood flow to different regions during specific tasks. This has enabled neuroscientists to understand brain structures and the processes involved in thinking and acting. Functional magnetic resonance imaging (fMRI) techniques have been used extensively to measure the effects of music on different areas of the brain.

Here's a quick crash course in how the brain works: Weighing just 3lbs, but containing over 100 billion nerve cells, the brain is composed of three main parts. The cerebrum is the largest and consists of left and right hemispheres. Regions within the cerebrum are responsible for functions such as interpreting touch, vision, hearing, speech, reasoning, learning, movement control and emotions. The cerebellum is smaller and located lower, underneath the cerebrum. It is responsible for the coordination of muscles to maintain posture, balance and achieve movement. Thirdly the brainstem relays instructions from the cerebrum and cerebellum to the spinal cord through the nerves.

The brain's nerve cells are called neurons. The nerve cells are grey-brown in colour, while the connecting fibres are white. Because the surface of the cerebrum (known as the cortex) is folded, the surface area is dramatically increased, allowing a high volume of neurons to fit inside our skull.

The left hemisphere controls the right side of the body and vice versa. Some functions are linked to one specific hemisphere. For instance, it is acknowledged that musical skills, creativity, spatial ability and artistic skills are controlled by the right hemisphere. The left hemisphere controls speech, comprehension, arithmetic, writing and is dominant in language and hand movements.

Each of the two hemispheres is divided into 4 lobes: frontal, temporal, parietal and occipital. These lobes do not function alone but in a complex relationship.

David Byrne in his book *How Music Works* noted that music triggers more neurons than many of the other arts. Multiple regions of the brain fire upon hearing music: muscular; auditory; visual; linguistic. This is an important distinction and the reason that I believe music is currently being greatly under utilised as an asset for health and wellbeing.

A UCLA study proposed that our appreciation and feeling for music are deeply dependent on mirror neurons. When you watch, or even just hear, someone playing an instrument, the neurons associated with the muscles required to play that instrument fire. As you might guess, the mirror neuron system lit up in the musicians who were tested, but surprisingly, it flashed in non-musicians as well.

Many different regions of the brain respond to and play a part in processing music. Daniel Levitin (2006) expands on this in his book *This is Your Brain on Music: The Science of a Human Obsession*. He says listening to music begins below the surface of the cerebrum in sub-cortical structures – the cochlear nuclei, the brain stem, the cerebellum. Then it moves up to the auditory cortices on both sides of the brain. All acoustic information enters the brain through the cochlear nuclei. The auditory cortices help break down this information into more sophisticated translation including pitch, timbre, spatial location and so on. Comparisons of these sounds are made with templates stored from previous experiences. There is a creation of expectations, and a violation and satisfaction of expectations.

The amygdala triggers the brain's emotional centre and frontal lobe. This triggers emotional reactions to music, and the release of neurotransmitter chemicals, such as dopamine, which make us feel good. The hippocampus plays its part in memory, musical experiences, and contexts. It has been identified that grey matter density of the hippocampus is often higher in musicians than in non-musicians. Foot tapping, dancing and playing an instrument (even air guitar) activate the motor cortex and sensory cortex. Reading music (or the lyrics) and watching a performance (even just the music video) work the visual cortex. The corpus callosum carries all of this information between the left and right hemispheres. Music gives the brain an extensive workout.

Cortisol, the hormone associated with stress and anxiety, can also be lowered by listening to music. Our heart rates and blood pressure also react positively to music. Listening to relaxing sounds helps produce a calm state. Recent interest in this area has led to a growing range of music products and binaural beats all claiming to produce relaxation states, help people manage anxiety and overcome panic attacks. However, I still maintain that this is a very personal result. The track titled *Weightless* by Marconi Union has in recent years been referred to as the most relaxing music in the world by the British Academy of Sound Therapy. But it has the opposite effect on me. So you need to find the low tempo music that works for you. Also make sure you choose an appropriate volume and not so loud that it's uncomfortable and challenging. Music certainly has the power to achieve these changes in mood and blood vessel dilation but the results are most impressive when you find the music that works for you.

These effects have been recorded since the late 1700s when the first known article (as far as I'm aware) titled *Music Physically Considered* was printed in the Columbian Magazine in 1789 and recommended the use of music in a therapeutic capacity to treat sick persons. In the 20th century music as a therapy was used widely during and after World War I. In 1915 Lena Ashwell, a Canadian born singer and actress, headed to the trenches to provide some musical relief for troops on the front line. Her diary entries described how performers would sit singing to the wounded after concerts had ended. In later years community musicians regularly performed in veterans' hospitals. The positive emotional effects of this intervention led to hospitals hiring musicians according to the American Music Therapy Association.

College curriculums sprung up around this music therapy field. However, hospital authorities also believed that because the community bands consisted of female musicians this also had a positive effect on the psychological condition of the wounded soldiers they were performing for. I'm sure that was indeed a contributing factor but now we have almost a century of additional evidence (from male and female musicians) that places no doubt on the positive effects that music can have on those suffering any level of anxiety, whether its post-traumatic stress from warzones or fear of exams.

Music has the ability to change mood, to build confidence, to manage anxiety, to bring people together into strong teams. Music has been integral to the military, to religious culture to the success of Olympic athletes. In environments where stress and anxiety is present music has historically been used to combat those anxieties. Today is no different. The body reacts in the same ways. Next time you feel the need to relax try it for yourself. There is a whole plethora of companies that peddle relaxation tapes. But for me personally I find that more upbeat music actually combats my anxiety and puts me immediately back in a positive mindset. I find relaxation tapes extremely irritating. It's a personal effect so you need to try a variety of music styles to find the one that works best for you. But when you find it you realize that it can be highly effective and most importantly FAST acting. Kapow! Every year more studies publish similar results. It's not news but it helps keep these facts in the public eye.

Music can also act as a cognitive distraction, which can help manage perceptions of pain. This is a similar effect to the way that music delayed the perceived onset of fatigue during exercise in my research in the 1990s. Current medicine is examining the role of music in pain management in more detail and the body of evidence is growing to support its use as a recognised tool for the management of both pain and depressive disorders. Music can help release endorphins into the blood stream which assist in producing a happy emotional state and can also assist in blocking pain. Listening to music can also release serotonin, a neurotransmitter produced in the brain stem that defends against mood problems and is key to our happiness.

Levitin, in a later review of related studies, says the scientific evidence supports claims that music influences health through neurochemical changes in four domains:

(i) reward, motivation and pleasure;
(ii) stress and arousal;
(iii) immunity; and
(iv) social affiliation.

He stated that these effects are due to the known neuro-chemicals that are affected by music such as dopamine, cortisol, serotonin, oxytocin, adrenaline and endorphins.

Perhaps the most startling fact in this journey of music is that outside of our body it doesn't exist at all. Music (and all sound) is simply the movement of air molecules. It's only when those air molecules reach our ear drum that our brain starts decoding it into something we know as music.

Music can be described as organised sound. It has certain structural elements that apply to all musical pieces such as loudness (amplitude/volume), rhythm (tempo and meter), pitch (musical notes, key), timbre (sound tone). Neuroscience research based on fMRI data proves that listening to (processing) music involves multiple areas of the brain. If you were to watch this response in real-time on a screen, the brain would literally be lighting up as it activates different regions during the process. Listening to music works the brain with a unique intensity. This can be an incredible tool, and the way in which it also triggers emotional responses and memories are only just beginning to be fully acknowledged and harnessed.

NYU Professor, neurologist and author Oliver Sacks was an ardent fan of music in health. In his book *Musicophilia* he wrote: "Our auditory systems and nervous systems are indeed exquisitely tuned for music. How much of this is due to the intrinsic characteristics of music itself and how much to special resonances, synchronisations, oscillations, mutual excitations or feedbacks in the immensely complex, multi-level neural circuitry that underlies musical perception and replay, we do not yet know." The contribution that Sacks made to music psychology is immense. He championed music as a vital part of the human experience. The brain processes it and reacts to it, despite the fact that it has no recognisable value to the continuation of life, as compared to food, water, and sex. In the words of Oliver Sacks:

"One does not need to have any formal knowledge of music – nor, indeed, to be particularly 'musical' – to enjoy music and to respond to it at the deepest levels. Music is part of being human, and there is no human culture in which it is not highly developed and esteemed."

Sacks likened our music responses to walking, running or swimming. We process or recall one note at a time but it is seamlessly connected to make the whole. Like making one step or stroke and it being an integral part of the whole rhythm of running or swimming.

Sacks was a pioneer in this field and if this chapter is sparking your interest in neuroscience and cognitive psychology I would highly recommend his *Musicophilia* book and Daniel Levitin's *This Is Your Brain On Music* for further reading material.

Music: the universal language

We all have our favourite music. These decisions are based on many variables outside of the music itself. Our social situation at the moment that we first experience these songs is particularly influential. The environmental situation, the location, the hormones, the experience - it all shapes how we remember music. So it's no surprise that music experienced during our early teens appears to be the most vivid in our long-term memory. It recalls special memories of school days, excitement, energy, fear and youth.

The importance of music on the brain was famously tested in the 1990s by playing Mozart music to teenagers before they tackled a cognitive test. The research claimed that listening to Mozart boosted intelligence (albeit only temporarily). This so called 'Mozart Effect' has been blown out of proportion in the decades since the study was published. It is acknowledged among scientists that it is music itself (not just Mozart) that produces these effects. If the researchers had used an Elvis song it could likely have produced the same effects and been coined 'The Elvis Effect'.

However, there is a large body of music that can produce very similar responses in people regardless of age, background, location. Uptempo music gives us the urge to dance. Low tempo, mellow music can make us relaxed. It can be a very unifying tool even where people are from different parts of our planet. It's a universal language. Research over the years suggests that our ability to follow rhythms is an innate skill and universal to all cultures. Our upbringing, however, does seem to create certain preferences. Those brought up immersed in Western music with regular metrical structures have a clear preference to this rather than to irregular rhythms that are more difficult to replicate. Whereas those who were brought up in cultures where irregular rhythms were common had much less bias between the two styles. So the simplistic styles of western rock and pop styles for instance can be easily absorbed by all cultures. They have achieved global success.

Can Artificial Intelligence Compose Songs That Produce The Same Brain Responses?

I'm on the UK Parliamentary Group for Artificial Intelligence. We meet at the House of Lords regularly throughout the year to hear experts in technology, law, social issues and medicine present their evidence about the future effects of artificial intelligence on the economy and society. A growing number of new companies as well as established organisations such as Google and Sony are racing to perfect artificial intelligence that can write music as well as a human can. They aim to do this by training the machines to learn the concepts of composition by reading through extensive databases of music.

By studying and comparing these songwriting structures and patterns it is possible for the machine to then create its own musical scores. These are then played by human musicians or produced electronically by the machine itself. But can this really produce the same effects on the human brain as human compositions? In some instances this appears to be the case.

Repetitive beat-driven instrumental compositions used in gaming and as background music appear almost indistinguishable. But when it comes to lyric and vocal-based compositions the technology still seems to have a long way to go to compete with a human composer. But AI is very fast-paced so this technology could achieve a much more sophisticated output in a short space of time. Watch this space. For now though it looks like we are a little way off any award winning hits. In 2016 there was a flurry of excitement about the new West End musical *Beyond The Fence* that was being composed by a computer. The excitement was short lived, with critics giving less than glowing reviews and using descriptions such as "sweetly bland".

So the science really does show that listening to music not only gives your brain an exceptional workout, but also can result in a range of short and long-term benefits. From pain relief to dementia prevention, anxiety management to improved circulation and reduced blood pressure. Here's a few suggestions to help you get more music in your daily routines.

HOW DO I APPLY THIS IN LIFE?

In Daily Life

The beauty of music in today's society is that it is easily accessible and affordable. Getting more music into your daily life couldn't be easier. At its simplest you could just listen to more radio. Even if you're not dancing around to the music and it's only background, your brain is still processing the sounds - and lighting up all those different neural regions.

For a more intensive and active listening experience use headphones. Whether you're listening whilst on the move (using a portable player) or at home sitting in your favourite chair, headphones deliver an exceptional experience because they block other stimuli and really help the brain focus on the music. I'd choose this sort of brain workout over crosswords or Sudoku, but if you enjoy crosswords and Sudoku why not do them whilst listening to background music.

If you're in the car stock up on a range of CDs or playlists. Vehicles are now one of the prime consumption points of music with many cars now featuring impressive high quality music systems for a great listening experience.

In terms of musical content it really doesn't matter what you listen to as it will all give your brain a workout. Choose music that you enjoy, whether you're streaming, using a turntable, or a CD player. If you're using a laptop or tablet or TV you could also immerse yourself in YouTube. However, research does indicate that new music rather than songs that are familiar to you can give the brain an even greater workout. It challenges the brain to process these unfamiliar songs and create new memories for future reference. Try switching to a different radio station or listening to other people's playlists. Head to your local record store and ask them to recommend some new music for you. There's plenty of it out there!

If you suffer from pain, depression or anxiety there is

growing scientific evidence regarding the ability of music to make a positive impact. Low dopamine (the feel-good chemical) can be a contributory factor in depression. It can also result in low levels of motivation and energy. Listening to music you enjoy releases dopamine. So in this sense background music may not have as much of an effect as music that you enjoy that you are actively, rather than passively, listening to.

In Business

Of course once you realise how effective music can be in manipulating a person's mood it goes without saying that these same positive effects can be harnessed in business. Think about how you can ensure that your customers come into contact with music during their purchase journey. It might be on hold during a phone call. It might be within a retail store setting. It might be in a restaurant or bar or gym. Think carefully about how you employ music as a tool so that you can enjoy the maximum benefits. The music selection needs to reflect your customer base - remember that music from people's youth has the most impact. If you have a broad demographic stick with mainstream pop rock that is most likely to be inoffensive and similar in style to music from past decades. Then think very carefully about the volume you choose and the quality of your technology. I have been on hold several times in the past (usually to insurance companies) listening to agonisingly loud music blaring in a really poor quality level down my telephone. If you get it right, music can deliver great results. But get it wrong on song choice, volume and sound quality, and you risk it having the opposite effect on customers.

There's a jukebox which has been installed at St Pancras International train station in London. It contains all the classic pop and rock hits and whenever I pass it (which is almost daily) there are always people selecting songs on it, such is the draw of music. Music can positively impact the productivity of your workforce as well as your customers. Think about how you can help your employees get more music in their lives. Are radios allowed at work? If this isn't appropriate is there an area where a radio could be located – for example in a kitchen area where staff go for breaks? Could you negotiate corporate deals on music streaming services or concert tickets? Educate your staff regarding the health effects of listening to music. The impact you have on their wellbeing while they are in the workforce will pay dividends in their later lives as well as their work productivity. Maintaining brain health throughout life is vitally important but usually neglected. People are fully aware of the fact that they should be eating healthily and exercising their bodies but brain health isn't usually addressed until a problem arises. Brain health should form part of our overall health programme.

3. Let Me Entertain You
*The health effects of performing
and creating music*

The positive physiological and psychological effects of creative expression and learning musical instruments are backed up by science. Creativity is good for you. This chapter outlines the reasons why.

I can't remember exactly what triggered my love of musical instruments but I do remember being quite obsessed with my uncle's acoustic guitar when I was very young. When visiting my grandparents' house I would sneak into his bedroom when he wasn't there and try to play it. It was far too large for me, but he had a guitar tutorial book by Ulf Goran and I can remember trying to strum along to *House of the Rising Sun* and *Drunken*

Sailor. I eventually got a guitar of my own and continued teaching myself to play along to songs on my record player. The breakthrough was when I bought my first 45rpm single in 1977 – *Mull of Kintyre* by Wings. It was the Christmas number 1 single and spent 9 weeks at the top of the charts, becoming the first UK single to sell over 2 million copies, the best selling single of all time. I played it over and over, practising my chord changes. The song structure was slow and simple; a very simple strumming pattern with just a few basic chords. The ideal song for a beginner. I felt like a pro playing along with the record. Other songs I liked were gradually added to my repertoire.

My primary school didn't teach guitar so my only formal lessons were on the recorder and violin. They were dreadfully dull. I loved music but had no interest in learning to read music notation, or playing classical compositions. I had already taught myself how to play along to the greatest hits of the era on my guitar. I ditched the violin lessons as soon as I was allowed to, bought my first electric guitar, a bass guitar, got together with some pals at school and formed my first pop rock band. This was supremely exciting. I remember that my bass amplifier was absolutely enormous – a 100 watt large combo unit on wheels. My mum had an ancient Mini Clubman that this would just about squeeze into when the seats were dropped. When I used to practice at home the bass would reverberate throughout the house, making ornaments in the lounge and the glass panel in the bathroom door vibrate. I wasn't remotely interested in the music lessons that I was forced to attend at primary school and later at grammar school. The teachers were uninspiring, the music we were told to learn and play was boring classical content that I didn't identify with at all. During my PhD field work I found that I was certainly not alone in these experiences. I heard similar memories from almost every respondent. Music tuition in the 1960s, '70s and '80s didn't capture the passions of the teenagers of the time. Now aged 40-70 this cohort (according to the responses to my PhD survey and interviews) wishes they had learned to play an instrument when they were a child. It was sad to see these trends emerge from the research. The schools could have so easily tapped into the immense music passion of these generations. Music was their life. It was how they forged their identity as teenagers. Their tribes driven by a myriad of music subcultures. But the curriculum wasn't designed for them. It was designed for a bygone era and it was too inflexible to change.

Interestingly, despite the fact that most respondents wished they could play an instrument very few were actually now having lessons. Even though they have the time and the disposable income. Without doubt, being able to play an instrument is an amazing experience. It's a skill that stays with you for life. I strongly believe that it is far more important to teach lots more low skilled amateur musicians than lots more professional ones. You really don't need to be able to play more than a few chords on guitar or keyboards (or basic beats on a drum kit) to get enjoyment and health benefits from an instrument. You certainly don't need to be able to read musical notation. This is why it seems puzzling that, according to my interviews and experience, many music lessons and teachers (not all of course) still insist on taking new students through this slow learning curve using songs that simply don't inspire their young learners. If you want to encourage children to eat vegetables you start them off on the fun vegetables like peas or carrots or broccoli. You don't start with cabbage which is much less likely to match the tastes of children. You learn to love cabbage later in life. If you want to enthuse people about musical instruments you start with learning the hit songs they are most familiar with and **love**, not a composition by a classical composer or an old rocker they've never heard of.

The renowned French sociologist Bourdieu (1984) viewed education as a significant influencing variable in the formation of music tastes. It also influences arts funding decisions relating to public money, with the classical genre being the predominant benefactor. However, what became very obvious during conversations with the participants during my three years of field work was that they were mostly disengaged from formal music education in school during their childhood, despite the fact that they were all obviously very engaged with popular music during their leisure time. This highlights the potential failure of music education during the 1970s and 80s amongst this cohort. The music curriculum did not inspire or interest them. In fact in many cases it resulted in a rejection of the classical music curriculum because it was being forced upon them and ultimately on the whole they found it an un-enjoyable experience. The curriculum was heavily dominated by core classical works and notation. For the majority of the respondents this was not the music that they were immersed in at home.

The following responses below were collected from a number of individuals during the participant interviews, and highlight the long-term effect that this had on today's generation of school children from the 1960s to 1980s. The females now aged in their 40s said that "it was dry and didn't reflect my love of music in any way. I hated it. I also hated the instrument lessons after school. I would love to learn guitar or piano today". The same key words came up time and time again "I didn't **enjoy** them at all, not very **interesting**. I would love to learn to play piano." There was a distinct lack of fun evident in the responses "I didn't enjoy music lessons. They were far too serious. I learnt a bit of violin and clarinet but don't play today." In some cases people felt very strongly that they had missed out on learning to play an instrument in school because they had been effectively put off by the curriculum content "they were not at all inspirational and the teacher was crap!"

Nicola was the one exception in the female 40s participants. She had always had a love of music and still writes and records her own compositions in her spare time. She said "I loved music lessons, I loved sound and rhythm. I play guitar and drums and would love to play piano now too."

The men now aged in their 40s demonstrated similar feelings regarding the memories of their music education. "I didn't enjoy music at school at all, they only taught classical. We were not encouraged to play guitars etc. I'd love to learn guitar or piano." Many respondents used the same or similar words in their descriptions "I found them very boring. I had to learn violin." These men mirrored the views of the women in that they wished they could play an instrument. "Music lessons at school were ok but not great. I wanted to learn more than we were taught and then I lost interest. I wish I had learnt the piano and guitar when I was young." Jon was the only participant aged 40s who expressed a love of school music lessons and he learnt to play piano when he was young.

The men now in their 50s expressed similar experiences. "No I didn't enjoy music lessons, they weren't trendy". Music lessons weren't cool enough for the 1960s crowd who were becoming obsessed with the explosion of popular music genres in the 1960s and 1970s. "I don't remember them at all in primary school and what I do remember from Grammar school was very choir based. I'd love to play piano or guitar really well." Again, despite the fact that these guys were in school almost a decade before the respondents now aged 40s, the same memories were emerging. "Music at school was very boring and I never learnt any instruments until I left. I taught myself a bit of guitar". The exception was Chris who enjoyed his music lessons as it was his "best subject". He clearly had a talent for instruments and learnt piano, violin, viola and organ during his teens. Today he also plays piano and guitar and earns his living as a professional musician across both classical/choral and contemporary work.

Dee and Margaret had positive music experiences at

school. In Dee's case it was largely due to having a great music teacher that helped her enjoy the lessons. Margaret was in the school choir and really enjoyed singing with her mum in the church choir so that was a key factor in her frequency of participation. In her case the music taught in school was very similar to the music she heard at home. All of the above quotations are taken from interviews and survey responses gathered during my PhD field work in 2011 – 2014. It was clear that music in school has a significant impact on lifelong music tastes but in fact it was the music that they shared in lunch breaks and after school that left the lifelong imprints, not what they were exposed to in their formal music lessons.

I am Trustee of the charity arm of the phenomenally successful Young Voices Concerts. Every year we sell out multiple nights at UK and USA arenas. Hundreds of thousands of primary school pupils and their teachers pack the stadium and sing the pop and rock songs they have learnt during the term (using the teaching packs that Young Voices send to the schools). It's an incredible experience. Popular music styles haven't changed much in six decades. Catchy melodies and simple lyrics proved a winning formula for kids in the 1950s and they still do in the 2010s. Providing music that children (and adults) love is the key to winning their enthusiasm, their passion and their time.

Feversham Primary School in Bradford, England with a history of poor results and low staff and parent morale turned to music and achieved incredible results. The headteacher, Naveed Idrees, admitted that this new approach was "a big risk" but is now convinced that this focus on music could transform other schools too. He introduced up to 6 hours of music a week to the school timetable. The school's test scores have improved dramatically and attendance by the 510 pupils increased to 98% as the amount of music taught to each pupil has risen. This year 74% of the school's pupils achieved the expected standard in reading, writing and maths, against a national average of 53%. These results are even more spectacular because 99% of pupils speak English as a second language. Idrees hopes that other schools will realise that music and creative subjects are not an add-on but essentials for skills development, motivation, engagement and pupil progress.

Why learning an instrument is an excellent brain work-out

Scientific research shows that learning and playing an instrument has a significant and positive effect on our brains. Studies have shown that these effects can even play a part in the possible prevention of dementia in later life. Playing an instrument involves both the brain and the activation of the limbs plus all core muscles to aid posture. The brain controls the motor movements of the musculature to produce the sounds. The feedback loop via the auditory centre adjusts the fine motor movement accordingly if necessary. All the while sensory information is being fed back to the brain for processing. The fingers and eyes deliver constantly updated information regarding the performance. There are also emotional responses to the music that's being produced.

Learning an instrument produces permanent structural changes in the brain due to the activity that this task involves. New neurons can be formed as new experiences are logged in the brain and stored for future reference. The more these pathways are triggered, the stronger they become. This repetition process (known to us as 'practice') is essential for learning and memory, especially in the hippocampus region of the brain. Many studies using functional magnetic resonance imaging (fMRI) have identified the effect of musical training on the structure and organisation of the human brain.

The brain undergoes continual modification both during childhood and through adulthood. This ability of the brain to modify its functional organization and structure is known as 'plasticity'. Music is known to be a highly effective model for studying plasticity because the learning process is often started early in life during school years when the brain is still developing. The process of making music also involves multiple executions from many regions of the brain. It can be a very effective tool for facilitating and encouraging brain plasticity throughout life.

A comprehensive longitudinal study in 2013 found that "music improves cognitive and non-cognitive skills more than twice as much as sports, theatre or dance." The study found that children taking music lessons had better cognitive skills, were more conscientious and ambitious and that it resulted in better school grades.

Several studies have also examined the effects of learning

music on language acquisition and found that music lessons strengthen the skills needed for learning language, such as the ability to learn sound patterns, rhythm perception and auditory memory. These language skills contributed to reading development and verbal skills. And that's not all. Music lessons were also shown to improve mathematical skills. This shouldn't be surprising as music is very mathematic in terms of its structure and relationship to scales, keys and rhythms. Studies found that children who receive music training often tend to score higher in mathematical tests, due to their improved spatial-temporal skills.

So music improves language skills and maths skills - arguably two of the most important skills for any career. There continues to be a range of studies that demonstrate a very strong correlation between music training and academic grades (and IQ scores). Exposure to music lessons before the age of 7 seems to have a particularly positive effect on the connectivity of the *corpus callosum*. It also helps fine motor skill development, especially finger dexterity because musical instruments require intense involvement of the motor cortex. Music has also been shown to improve memory and reasoning abilities, helping students to remember more content. Additionally music learning has been shown to produce greater abilities to cope with anxiety, aggression, attention deficit, depression and to enhance self-confidence and self-esteem. Studies have shown a particular thickening of the cortex in regions known to be associated with the control of anxiety and behaviour.

Music training enhances communication between the right and left hemispheres of the brain. This complex use of both hemispheres is known to be linked with creative thinking, giving individuals the ability to come up with new solutions to problems and tasks. Music practice and learning is known to cause the growth of myelin in the brain. Without getting too "science-y" here let's just say that this produces a boost that speeds up and strengthens signals that are travelling to their destinations. It's like upgrading from a dial up internet connection to broadband. It's faster and more efficient. Studies show that there is a correlation between the amount of practice musicians do and the density of their white matter (myelin). The key to enhanced performance is to match the quantity of practice with the quality of practice. Without effective feedback and correction of mistakes practice can embed bad habits which later have to be broken.

Yet, despite all the scientific evidence, music is being stripped from the school curriculum. Cuts and reorganisations have put music at the back of the queue despite outrage from parents and musicians. Red Hot Chilli Peppers' bass player Flea told USA politicians that cutting music education programmes is child abuse. In the UK the University of Sussex in 2017 stated that based on their research findings music could face extinction in schools. We are most certainly witnessing a seriously worrying erosion. Music has been put under intense pressure since 2010 when the British government brought in new curriculum guidelines that effectively stifled the arts. English, maths, sciences, languages, geography and history have been prioritised in the face of decreasing budgets. These subjects are linked to the measures of a school's performance. Researchers at the University of Sussex found that 60% of music staff surveyed at state schools specifically said that the new government guidelines caused a negative effect on the provision and uptake of music at the school. Just 3% believe the changes had benefited the subject. Schools offering Music BTEC Level 2 fell from 166 in 2013 to just 50 in 2017. For students aged 13 to 14, music was compulsory in just 62% of schools, compared with 84% of schools in 2013. Experts at the University believe this erosion of music will continue unless the government takes action.

I mentioned earlier that I'm involved in the All Party Parliamentary Group for Artificial Intelligence. We meet at the House of Lords throughout the year to discuss matters that are related to the current and future effects of artificial intelligence on the country. My interest is twofold. Firstly, AI will impact the music industry in many ways, and it will also impact education. Recently in one House of Lords evidence session the topic of education was being discussed. All expert panel members agreed that arts subjects were equally as important as STEM subjects (science, technology, engineering and mathematics). I pointed out that the Parliamentary Group in their recent recommendations to the UK Government had listed (in 3rd place on their list!) that STEM subjects must be prioritized in curriculums. We all debated this and agreed that this in fact should say STEAM not STEM in order to recognize the value that arts subjects deliver. This is because many of the skills shortages that we are facing – in AI related business sectors – are communication and teamwork. Those skills are best taught through soft skills such as music, sport, art. The very subjects that are being squeezed out of curriculums! This does not make sense. The CEO of gigantic Chinese e-commerce company AliBaba at the recent Davos Conference in 2018 also reiterated these facts. He urged people to realize that music and sports are vital in developing people who have the ability to work together, communicate well and also have soft skills that can't be replicated by machines.

There is now intense research interest into the effect of creativity in adulthood. This is partly driven by the ageing population and the potential cost to the economy if we don't age well. Given that music learning and music playing during childhood produces such significant cognitive effects, music could have a leading role to play in the prevention of health decline throughout your whole life. I truly believe this. Hence why I've written this book to help people access all the evidence that backs up this fact.

According to many research studies, learning to play a musical instrument is beneficial for children and adults alike, and may even be helpful to patients recovering from brain injuries. "Music probably does something unique," explains neuropsychologist Catherine Loveday of the University of Westminster. "It stimulates the brain in a very powerful way, because of our emotional connection with it. Music reaches parts of the brain that other things can't. It's a strong cognitive stimulus that grows the brain in a way that nothing else does, and the evidence that musical training enhances things like working memory and language is very robust."

For adults who were forced to attend music lessons each week during childhood this is good news. There is good reason to believe that the plasticity effects on your brain are long lasting and can be refreshed with new practice. So you've already got some dormant skills and knowledge that will give you a head start. You'll be amazed at how quickly you can pick up those old music skills, even though it may have been decades since you last played the instrument.

But how can music performance and creation prevent physical decline? The decline of our muscle mass starts to occur from our mid 40s and can lead to reduced strength, decreased quality of life, increased risk of injury and eventually increased care costs as we become weaker and more frail.

Resistance exercise has been shown to decrease frailty and improve muscle strength in very elderly adults. Exercise is recommended on most days of the week, but a minimum of three times per week is recommended to slow muscle loss - called sarcopenia, which is one of the biggest benefits of exercise as we age (we'll look at sarcopenia in more detail in a later chapter examining music and exercise).

We are often encouraged to do more exercise to combat the ageing process. However, older adults tend to lean towards aerobic activity rather than weight training. This is largely because awareness campaigns focus more on aerobic exercise activity. Research agrees that weight training is equally as important (possibly more important) in later life as aerobic activity. It prevents weakness and falls. I just recently (aged 47) have taken up power lifting. It sounds bizarre I know but the three core lifts – squat, bench press and dead lift – are compound exercises that use lots of muscles at the same time. Lifting heavy weights triggers muscle and bone growth so can defy muscle loss and osteoporosis in later life. Music plays an exceptional role when pushing yourself like this. When I first entered this space I felt out of place and vulnerable. A little stupid actually. But the video screens were displaying footage of men and women achieving successful lifts against a backing track of beat driven music. When I focused on that I started to feel more confident and less out of place. Powerful music puts you in a "can do" mind space. It can elicit a "f#*# you" attitude and that can be very powerful. Men and women can continue power lifting well into their 80s. There is no reason why they should not. In fact the physiological evidence suggests that they absolutely should be doing this sort of exercise. But societal "norms" makes this weight lifting, and power lifting in particular, an exercise choice that few people – especially women – make. The belief (not true) is that you turn into a big bulging Popeye. This isn't the case at all for most people. You just maintain and build your STRENGTH and that's vitally important, especially as you age.

It's only recently that brain health decline has been given

similar attention to physical decline. Crosswords and puzzles are now recommended as brain trainers for the over-50s. So lots of retirees (and commuters!) now sit with a coffee and tackle the puzzle of the day in the daily newspaper. But learning a musical instrument at any age gives the brain a much more comprehensive workout than a crossword puzzle.

In Canada, BRAMS, the International Laboratory for Brain, Music and Sound Research, gives researchers access to MRI scanners and PET scanners. The centre exists to address questions such as: Why is the brain musical? How does the structure and function of the nervous system allow us to listen to, remember, play, and respond to music? How are these functions related to others such as understanding speech? How do these processes change during development, and how do they breakdown in disease?

The University of Southern California is actively studying the effect of ageing on the brain. Judy Pa is assistant professor at the USC Stevens Neuroimaging and Informatics Institute and the neurology department — both in the Keck School of Medicine of USC. The lack of pharmacological options for those suffering with Alzheimer's disease is what inspired Pa to develop the research project, LEARNit (Lifestyle Enriching Activities for Research in Neuroscience intervention trial), which looks into whether two modifiable lifestyle factors — physical and cognitive activity — can have an impact on brain health in people who have not been diagnosed with Alzheimer's but are at risk for the disease. "What we're looking for is a non-invasive way to help older adults keep their brains healthy," says LEARNit Project Manager Lisette Isenberg, who holds a PhD in cognitive neuroscience. "The goal is to see whether a relatively easy intervention, as opposed to going on a drug, is going to make a big difference in how their brain is able to function as they age." Isenberg says the ultimate goal for LEARNit is to figure out a way to delay the onset of Alzheimer's by 5 or 10 years. "Because then we could potentially find a cure, or patients could live a long and happy life without ever having to develop dementia," she says. "They can die of natural causes if we can delay it long enough. We are trying to preserve their quality of life." Pa continues: "If we can understand what combination of therapies has to occur so someone can maintain their cognitive status at the age of 60 or 65 or have it decline at a really slow rate until they're 85, that would be ideal." USC also has established a Brain and Creativity Institute focused on the effects of music on brain development (especially in childhood) and emotional responses.

It's not too late to benefit even if you didn't take up an instrument until later in life. Jennifer Bugos, an assistant professor of music education at the University of South Florida, Tampa, studied the impact of individual piano lessons on adults between the ages of 60 and 85. After six months those who had received piano lessons showed more robust gains in memory, verbal fluency, the speed at which they processed information, planning ability, and other cognitive functions, compared with those who had not. A great incentive to book some music lessons don't you think!

This burgeoning field is attracting plenty of additional work, such as Hervé Platel, a professor of neuropsychology at the Université de Caen Basse-
-Normandie, France, who is carrying out a neuroimaging study of healthy, ageing non-musicians just beginning to study a musical instrument.

The benefits above don't just apply to physical musical instruments. Even when we use our voice and sing out loud there are a multitude of benefits. While there are no finger movements to remember, control of the muscles that keep us in tune and maintain tone need fine adjustments too. Plus the lungs get an exceptional workout, which in turn assists our cardio-vascular circulation and health.

As humans we used to sing all the time. Work songs have been around for centuries – even Snow White's seven dwarves whistled while they worked, because research shows that it decreases boredom, alleviates monotony of repetitive tasks, builds team spirit and decreases errors and accidents (partly because of the delayed onset of fatigue and boredom). Religious songs have been around for even longer and enabled leaders to build strong followings. Folk songs, military songs, educational songs, anthems. Communities were built around singing and dancing. It enabled humans to connect in a synchronised way. Musical instruments carved from animal bones have been found that date back tens of thousands of years. Ancient paintings also feature musicians and dancers so it is accepted that music was always a part of life. Hence why it produces similar neural effects to fight or flight triggers, or food, or sex, despite it not having a direct impact on human survival. Sadly, despite our heritage somewhere along the way modern life, particularly in the western world, has made us more reticent about singing. We have become more self-conscious and scared of embarrassing ourselves. The beneficial health effects of singing occur even if the quality of singing isn't very good. So all the more reason to put on our favourite song and sing along even if we are a bit "pitchy", as Simon Cowell would say. Many research projects over several decades have shown that singing can improve our wellbeing and help boost a sense of happiness. These effects are multiplied when we sing in groups or choirs because of the additional social effects and feelings of belonging. This improved mood is largely due to the release of positive neurochemicals such as endorphins, dopamine and serotonin which help regulate mood and make us feel good.

The effects certainly increase when you sing in a group. Scientists have linked these social affiliation effects to oxytocin and prolactin released by the brain. Community choirs have grown in popularity in recent years. This is largely due to more people knowing about the health benefits of singing. But also it's been easier to bring a wide range of ages together using music, because three generations have now grown up with pop and rock styles. I absolutely would love to see many more choirs start to pop up in communities.

HOW DO I APPLY THIS IN LIFE?

In Daily Life

If you had music lessons when you were younger or used to play an instrument, dust off those skills and start to play again. You'll be back in the swing of it in no time at all. Sign up for some refresher lessons, find a local open mic night to hang out with and meet local amateur and professional musicians. If you see a piano in the street, have a little tinkle of the ivories. The appearance of street pianos has been one of the most successful initiatives in recent years. The pianos I see during my commute through St Pancras International station in London are rarely quiet. I see all ages playing on there and despite the age of the player, it's almost always a pop or rock hit. The most important thing is to not give two hoots about what people think. Don't be embarrassed. Just get involved.

If you have children or grandchildren, encourage them to have music lessons. The research shows that learning during childhood has particularly long-lasting positive effects, especially if they continue for 10 years. Even better, learn together and play together. This produces even more benefits.

If you feel confident enough, take to the stage. If you can't get to grips with learning an instrument from scratch, try DJing. It's a lot of fun and also produces cognitive benefits without having to learn how to play a musical instrument. The learning curve of learning to use the DJ equipment is shorter than learning to play an instrument.

Joining a choir is also really enjoyable and results in not only the mental benefits of music, but has social benefits too. If there isn't a local choir, why not gather some friends together and start one? I think this is an important next step in the evolution of music engagement. So let's bust some myths here. To gain a health benefit you do not have to be good, you don't even have to be in tune, you don't need a trained professional. However, hiring a musician or a singing teacher will help you pick a date to get started and make it more probable that you will continue. The important thing to remember is that it's the act of singing together that's important, it doesn't have to be highly technical. Don't worry about music notation or melodies and harmonies, just find a great song that you all enjoy and know well and start singing it together. You could even just sing along to the record, or download a karaoke backing track. In the early stages a few glasses of wine usually help as it relaxes people and helps them shake off their inhibitions. Just enjoy it.

In Business

Does your company have a workforce wellbeing programme? If it does I'll bet it's mainly focused on physical exercise rather than brain health. You've probably negotiated a corporate deal on the local gym membership rates. Maybe you also offer some fitness classes on site during lunch breaks or after work. Now that you've read about all the incredible health benefits that music can deliver to the brain and the importance of delaying cognitive decline throughout life, perhaps you will now want to expand your wellbeing programme to include music.

Contact local music teachers and invite them on site so that your staff members can have a weekly music lesson during their lunch break or after work. The beauty of music lessons is that the end result is a skill you acquire and possess forever. Whereas a series of fitness classes will produce a physical effect but will fade in time if that activity isn't continued. Giving your staff music lessons is a gift.

Start an in-house choir that your workforce can get involved in. Run some leadership, motivational or health workshops that involve singing so there is a natural progression from that into the ongoing choir. Group drumming can also be popular and equally effective, and requires less prior knowledge of songs or vocal skill.

Find out which employees are already musical and who may be in bands. Invite them to perform at one of your office social events or Christmas party. Sponsor them so they can go on tour. Feature them on your website. Champion any engagement with music to encourage others to do so too. Remember it is the engagement that is important, not the level of skill. We need to break down the barrier that stops people getting involved because they think they are not talented enough. I despair at the number of times people say to me that they "can't sing". Everyone can sing. If you can talk you can sing. In fact studies have shown that patients who have lost their speech capability, due to stroke or brain injury for example, are still able to sing sentences.

Do you have a loyalty programme for customers? What sort of incentives do you offer? Discounts on a range of products and experiences probably. Do any of them feature music offers? If not add them in. Negotiate deals on musical instruments and tuition. Invite local performers into stores or to perform outside your store entrance. My company curates live music experiences like this for retail businesses all across London. It's incredibly popular with customers and staff.

4. LET'S DANCE
The health effects of moving to music

Humans have moved in time with the rhythm of music for tens of thousands of years. We have danced and exercised to these sounds for generations. There are now many ways in which you can enjoy the physical health benefits that music delivers. This chapter examines these positive effects and some of the most popular activities.

Our ancient ancestors began moving in time to music when they started to dance. Unlike farming and hunting (which left behind stone tools that have been found dating back over 1 million years) dancing and music left less permanent traces. Flutes found in Southern Germany made from bird bone and mammoth ivory are thought to be the earliest musical instrument found so far. Carbon dating estimates they are approximately 40,000 years old. In India the cave paintings at the Bhimbetka rock shelters date back approximately 30,000 years and show that music and dancing were a part of everyday life. This is now a UNESCO World Heritage Site. Experts share the opinion that dance was a form of social bonding. It aided communication and expressed emotion. It was part of rituals and ceremonies and promoted healing. In comparison the earliest evidence of written language only dates back approximately 5,000 years so before its arrival music and dance are believed to have been an important method of connecting and communicating. When language began to develop traditional songs would have enabled stories and knowledge to be passed orally from generation to generation. This tradition continues today. The oldest known British folk song dates back to around 1260 and is thought to have been written at either Oxford or Reading Abbey. The lyrics describe the spring season and contain the first written appearance of the word 'fart'. Academics are unsure whether the song is an innocent description of nature or a slightly bawdy song. It's quite an uplifting little number. You can find it on the internet. I recognised the tune immediately because we used to sing it in primary school. It also featured in the horror film 'The Wicker Man'.

The ancient Greeks believed that dance was invented by the gods. They held it in extremely high regard. Dancing skills were a sign of good education and good physical skills (important for battle too). Socrates, the legendary Greek philosopher who lived from 470-399BC, said "whoever would have his body supple, easy and healthful should learn to dance." Socrates actually learned to dance in later life because he felt he'd missed out and wanted to improve the health of his aging body. Plato, his student, lived from 428-348BC and also appreciated dance and song, saying "the Dance, of all the arts, is the one that most influences the soul. Dancing is divine in its nature and is the gift of God. To sing well and to dance is to be well educated."

Wise words from these two important Greek philosophers. There is evidence in their writing that the ancient Greeks made therapeutic use of music. For example, listening to music at the end of the day to calm down and ensure a good night's sleep. The recognition of the power of music was also shared by Plato's student Aristotle who lived from 384-322BC. Aristotle, Plato and Socrates lived on this planet around 2,400 years ago. Centuries later, dance has now effectively slipped from centre stage, especially in adulthood. During my PhD research most of my survey participants aged over 40 told me that they very rarely dance except at family weddings. This illustrates a significant decline in the social and health value placed on dancing. It no longer features as an important and frequent part of our daily lives. This is surprising given the huge popularity it still enjoyed just a few decades ago. In 2017 research published in the Preventative Medicine journal stated that Britain has experienced its biggest ever recorded decline in dancing over the past decade. The proportion of men dancing has fallen by half, and the proportion of women dancing by a third.

At the turn of the 20th century, social dancing still played a central part in society. The more formal ballroom dance styles were superseded by exciting moves that matched the new musical sounds that were evolving. The 1920s featured the arrival of The Charleston, an energetic dance craze during the jazz era that produced outcry amongst older generations. It was the arrival of swing music in the 1940s though that took social dancing to a whole new level. These jive moves continued to evolve through the 1950s as rock and roll took over the dance floors. In the 1970s it was the arrival of the disco sound that once again put dance culture at the centre of our social scenes. Through the 1980s and 1990s dance clubs evolved into nightclubs, the opening hours were extended through into early mornings, the sounds became heavier and louder.

The dance styles may have changed over the decades, but one thing united them all - they were very much tied to youth culture. As people grew older, they aged out of those scenes and no longer danced. Yet interest in dancing still exists, as we can see through the enormous popularity of the BBC's *Strictly Come Dancing* television series and live tour, which attracted its highest ever viewing figures in its 2017 finale despite now being in its 14th year. In December 2017 a whopping 13.1 million people tuned in to see who won the annual contest. So why have we become spectators (from our armchairs) rather than active participants on the dance floors of Britain that still survive? I believe there are several reasons for this current situation. The health data that I presented in previous chapters suggests that perhaps this is tied to the general trend of inactivity that we are witnessing in adults. However, there are also social reasons. For instance, venues don't really exist for older adults to regularly dance at, and it's not something we are socially programmed to do in our adult life. If we made an effort to look for them we would find places locally that play music from our youth and have a dance floor. We need to reset the social norms and get back on the dance floor. I lose count of the number of people (usually men) who say that they are "rubbish at dancing". Since when did it become a competition? It doesn't matter how good you are. Even if you are just shuffling around and not even in time with the music you'll be getting a health benefit as long as you're enjoying yourself. We need to shake off the shackles of embarrassment that society has placed on us.

We've already talked about the significant psychological benefits and the brain responses to music in previous chapters. Hopefully, once this chapter reminds you of all the additional physical benefits that moving to music can deliver, you'll be inspired to get back out there and start shaking your stuff again. If you just can't bring yourself to dance then there are lots of other ways to move to music. We'll take a look at those too.

How Does Moving To Music Help My Bones?

In the 1990s I taught Anatomy & Physiology to undergraduates. I also taught Sport and Exercise Psychology. There was a marked difference between my preparation each year. As a subject, the psychology field was still developing rapidly, whereas, there have always been 206 bones in the adult human body. 80 of those bones make up our axial skeleton (skull, ribcage and spine) and the remaining 126 bones make up our appendicular skeleton (limbs and shoulder and hip girdles). More than half of those 206 bones can be found in our hands and feet. This is what enables us to grip and balance so precisely.

Our bone mass density - the indicator of bone health - peaks around the age of 30. When our bones lose density they are more prone to fracture, so maintaining good bone density is key to staying healthy and fit.

Diet plays an important part in maintaining bone density, with Calcium and Vitamin D being vital ingredients. You should be able to get all the calcium you need by eating a varied and balanced diet. Good sources of calcium include: milk, cheese and other dairy foods; green leafy vegetables, such as broccoli, cabbage and okra; soya beans; tofu; soya drinks with added calcium; nuts; bread and anything made with fortified flour; and fish where you eat the bones, such as sardines and pilchards. Spinach, although green and leafy so might appear to contain a lot of calcium, also contains oxalic acid which reduces calcium absorption.

It's difficult to get all the vitamin D we need from our diet, so we also get it from the action of the sun on our skin. Short daily periods of sun exposure without sunscreen from late March/April to the end of September are enough for most people to make enough vitamin D. However, it's sometimes necessary to consider taking a daily vitamin D supplement if exposure to sun is low.

Good sources of vitamin D include: oily fish, such as salmon, sardines and mackerel; eggs; fortified fat spreads; fortified breakfast cereals; some powdered milks.

Failure to supply your body with enough calcium and vitamin D throughout life will result in gradual loss of bone density. Over time bones become weaker and more susceptible to fractures. Unfortunately because this happens deep inside our bodies most people are not aware that this loss of bone density is happening until they get a fracture that is caused by osteoporosis. It's a slow and silent disease. The National Osteoporosis Society estimates around 3 million people in the UK have osteoporosis. This condition leads to bones becoming fragile and breaking easily, resulting in pain and disability. According to medical data 1 in 2 women and 1 in 5 men over the age of 50 will break a bone as a result of osteoporosis.

So in addition to paying more attention to our diet what else can be done to prevent or slow down bone loss as we age?

Exercise is absolutely key to maintaining bone density. However, it only has a positive effect if the exercise is weight-bearing (your own body weight) or against a resistance (for example, using weights or a resistance band). Swimming and cycling, although excellent for your cardiovascular fitness and weight control, are not as effective for maintaining bone density as hiking or running or tennis. Exercise works because bone is a living tissue, it consists of cells that are being created and broken down. Just like with your muscles, if more cells are broken down than created, the bone will decrease in density and strength, and vice versa. Putting the bones under pressure in exercise situations forces them to respond by building strength. Chris Hadfield, Commander of the International Space Station, attended an event we ran a few years ago. During his interview on stage he explained that from the moment they arrive in the zero gravity environment the body starts breaking down the skeleton, because in zero gravity there is no strain being placed upon it. The skeleton is no longer needed. The amount of calcium being lost from the body is measured in the urine. They use exercise equipment on board to try and slow that process down.

So where does music come into play here? As we've already seen, music can help us to exercise for longer, mainly because it makes the exercise experience more pleasurable due to the effects it has on the brain. It also distracts us from feelings of fatigue, so tricking the brain into continuing the exercise for longer. This has helped the exercise to music industry thrive over the past few decades. With a constant evolution of styles there are now many different exercise to music classes to choose from in local gyms and health clubs. Most involve weight-bearing exercises and are led by an instructor. These repetitive motions can play a key role in combating bone density loss. There are also options such as Zumba and salsa-themed workouts focused more on dance moves and routines than typical exercise based movements.

If group exercise to music classes don't appeal to you

don't worry. There are also exercises you can do solo. Music can play an important role here too because, as previously mentioned, it's proven that if you listen to music you enjoy while exercising it can help you to exercise for longer. So whether you're going out for a brisk walk (casual strolling isn't effective so really put some effort into it) or a jog, lifting some weights or doing some press ups, music can help boost the results.

Dancing is the ultimate workout because it fires the brain as well as the entire body and can also produce important social effects. Any dance, any style, any music, anywhere, anytime. It's worked for thousands of years and it still works.

Dr Kate Ward, a Senior Research Scientist at MRC Human Nutrition Research in Cambridge says "we do know that certain types of dance are weight-bearing and that weight-bearing exercise helps to build and maintain bones and muscles. As well as this, dancing may help maintenance of a healthy weight and balance, which are also important as we get older to prevent falls and fractures."

Dawn Skelton, a Professor of Ageing and Health at Glasgow Caledonian University, says the impact on bones through dance is one of its most important benefits. "Dancing should help improve bone strength," she says. "Most studies have shown potential effects on the spine."

Dance does improve balance and many other risk factors for falls, meaning even if the effect on bone is not strong, reducing the chances of falling has a helpful effect on reducing fracture rates. Some health authorities are so convinced about the positive effects of dance in terms of falls prevention that they are at last referring patients to dance classes. The Dance to Health initiative has trained dance instructors across the UK in two evidence-based falls prevention programmes that are embedded into dance lessons. The project is in its early stages but Tim Joss, Chief Executive of arts and health charity Aesop, which is behind the initiative, says he's hopeful the programme can be rolled out more widely in the future.

How Does Moving To Music Help Muscles and Soft Tissue?

The cellular density of our muscles also starts to decrease as we age. As we've already seen in previous chapters, this atrophying or wasting away of muscle cells is known as sarcopenia. The steady decline has become more of a widespread problem since our daily lives became increasingly sedentary. Our ancestors were much more active than us. Now we sit at our desk hunched over computers for several hours at a time. Poor posture can cause additional problems as some muscles become constantly overstretched and weakened while others become overly shortened and tight. This results in bones and joints misaligning and that triggers all sorts of painful issues. When this occurs many people turn to painkillers or massage rather than tackling the core issue of inactivity and putting more movement in their daily lives.

Fortunately, as with bone health, we can reverse or delay

the decline in muscle mass by adding regular weight-bearing or resistance exercises to our routines. Attention to diet is also important because protein is a vital ingredient for muscle cell growth. The muscles that hold our spine in alignment can deteriorate as we age and cause major back problems. The same is true for the muscle and tendons around the knee and hip joints. Being overweight further complicates the problems because unstable joints and the spine struggle to operate effectively in these conditions.

Mitochondria inside your muscle cells are responsible for aerobic metabolism to produce energy during exercise. If you have more of these little powerhouses inside your muscles, your muscles can produce more energy any time. When you put the body (bones and muscles) under pressure during exercise, your body responds by increasing the number of mitochondria. They dictate our calorie consumption. Someone with more mitochondria in their muscles burns more calories (even when just sitting down at rest) than a person with fewer mitochondria. Regular, long-term resistance training causes the fibres inside your muscles to grow. This doesn't mean you will suddenly have bulging muscles. The effects are based on how much resistance (overload) you put the body under and for how long. Dancing and exercise to music simply uses your body weight (unless you are carrying dumbells whilst doing it). Most people will notice that they feel more toned and stronger after a few weeks of general dancing or exercising to music.

How Does Moving To Music Help My Lungs and Circulation?

Nick Smeeton, a principal lecturer at the University of Brighton says "running, swimming and other propulsive forms of physical activity use rhythm and momentum to keep you moving. Whereas there is a lot of accelerating and decelerating in dancing, which the body is less able to do in an energy efficient way. If running is like driving on a freeway, dancing is more like motoring through a busy city. All of that starting, stopping and changing directions burns a ton of fuel even though you're not covering a lot of ground." Of course, it depends how much effort you're putting into your dance moves but Smeeton's study demonstrated that you could burn up to 300 calories in 30 minutes. Even moderate intensity dancing is thought to equal the calorie expenditure of a comparable period of cycling. In addition, the twisting movements and the side-to-side and forward-backward stepping help strengthen muscles and tendon-supporting joints.

Dancing forces our lungs to inhale greater amounts of air than usual in order to put sufficient oxygen back into the bloodstream to fuel the demand of the muscles. Other forms of aerobic exercise such as running also do this but a lot of people find dancing more fun than running and so are more likely to stick at it. Dancing is a whole body workout. That means there are a lot of muscles that need oxygenated blood to fire up the mitochondria. The heart has to work hard to keep delivering this oxygen from the lungs to the muscles. It has to circulate the blood quickly enough so that it can deliver fresh supplies of oxygen and transport the waste carbon dioxide back to the lungs to be exhaled and removed from the body. As with any aerobic exercise, the more often you do this activity, the more efficient the cardiovascular system becomes. When you start dancing you'll get out of breath if you put enough effort in. But after a few weeks of regular dancing you'll start to find it noticeably easier because your body has adapted. Your heart and lungs and network of blood vessels will improve. Researchers at the University of Maryland Medical Center also found a link between listening to music and heart health. They found that listening to joyful music is linked with dilation of blood vessels' inner lining, meaning more flow of blood through the blood vessels. Specifically, the diameter of blood vessels grew by 26% when a person listened to happy music. However, the opposite effect was noted when a person listened to anxiety-triggering music - blood vessel diameter decreased by 6% as a result.

The lungs can often get an even greater workout when we dance because often - if we're dancing to a song we like and are familiar with - we can start singing along. This requires very deep inhalation in order to get sufficient oxygen to feed the muscles and produce an exhalation that also projects a loud singing voice. This deep breathing works the muscles that lift the rib cage, giving them a good workout too.

The smallest blood vessels are the ones that enter the actual muscle tissue, called capillaries. Regular exercise results in more capillaries, meaning they are able to deliver more oxygen more efficiently through the muscle fibres. These changes and the resulting increased efficiency can be easily observed by reductions in resting heart rate and blood pressure readings.

HOW DO I APPLY THIS IN LIFE?

In Daily Life

The simplest way to use music to help improve your physical health would be to grab a pair of headphones and increase your daily walking levels. You've probably heard that you should be aiming to clock up 10,000 steps each day to achieve health benefits. Although this isn't strictly proven it's certainly a 'step' in the right direction. Buy a pedometer or a fitness tracker and prepare to be shocked when you realise how few steps you usually accumulate in a normal day. If that's the case it's time to make some changes to your daily routine.

At first 10,000 steps can seem an endless goal. This is where music can help. Pop your headphones on before your next walk. Not only will this boost your brain before you leave the house but it should keep you going for the full distance too. It's a great opportunity to listen to albums that you haven't heard for years from start to finish. You can also sing along if the mood takes you. Who cares what people think! Try and put as much effort as you can into the walking so that you get maximum benefits. Strolling is a good start but it will produce less benefits in terms of bone, heart and lung health. Set a brisk pace and try and include some uphill sections in your routes.

Some people often find it easier to get into a routine by joining a gym or signing up to a series of exercise to music classes. Motivation is key here because, as we've already seen in an earlier chapter, membership retention rates are pretty poor. People give up because they don't see immediate results. This is why it's essential to find a class or a gym that you absolutely love. Music can play a huge role in this. If the music matches your tastes you'll enjoy the experience of attending classes and gyms much more, and therefore are more likely to continue going.

Personally I'd like to see everyone of all ages starting to do more dancing again. I think this would produce a dramatic positive change in public health – physical and mental. However, many of the original dance venues have closed down and the remaining ones often don't specialise in an all-ages experience. They market to younger demographics, leaving older adults finding them quite daunting. If your local venue isn't catering for an older audience why not ask them if they might consider it? These venues are businesses after all. If they become aware that there is a market gap then they might agree to fill it. Outdoor dancing is especially beneficial as you are also getting the benefit of the sunshine.

In business

If your workforce wellbeing programme already has a

corporate deal in place with a local gym get in touch with the local exercise to music instructors and invite them to do some sessions at your workplace. These taster sessions can help people overcome the barrier of first attending a session. It can be very intimidating joining a class as a newbie when everyone else already knows all the moves. If your employees have already experienced the class at their place of work they will feel less intimidated about attending it for the first time at the gym.

Even better, why not start a dance club or offer some dance lessons to your employees? According to the Office for National Statistics 137.3 million working days were lost due to sickness in 2016. This equates to an estimated cost of £29 billion. The three main causes of absence were colds, musculo-skeletal issues and mental health issues. So workforce wellbeing really is worth focusing on if you want your company to achieve peak performance. Dancing improves social bonds amongst employees and delivers important physical and emotional benefits.

If your business is a music business think about the core population of your catchment area. What's the demographic profile? Would there be a market for a 1950s dance night, 1960s dance night, 1970s disco night etc? Maybe even some daytime dance sessions and events? If you own large retail areas or open spaces think about doing some dance lessons or dance sessions to attract customers into or onto your premises. Once they are there they might also buy something else from you. Do you have a loyalty programme for customers? Why not offer some local dance lessons or event tickets?

If you're a local council make sure you are making every effort to help people get as much dancing into their daily lives as possible. Engage with your local venues, support them and encourage them to programme for all ages with daytime events for older residents. Encourage local DJs and musicians to perform outdoors and create great environments where people can congregate and dance together. Popular music now engages three generations so it can be very effective. Create closer relationships with all the music businesses and musicians in your town or city. Form a Music Board to help support the music ecosystem and allow music and dancing to thrive. Help nurture a strong street performance programme in your town and city centres. You have the power and resources to help facilitate more access to music and dancing opportunities.

We are humans. We were born with the ability to dance and to sing. We need to learn to let go of the inhibitions modern society has injected into us and let our hair down again. Do everything you can to help your employees, staff and local residents achieve this.

5. RELAX

The critical importance of rest and sleep and how music can help us get more of it

Music and rest are already entwined. I remember learning about rest in music lessons at primary school. I had no real desire to learn how to read the black dots of music notation. I was already teaching myself guitar using basic chord diagrams. That was much easier and more fun. It enabled me to play along to Blondie songs within no time at all. However, my teachers (and family) seemed intent on my acquisition of violin playing skills and so I dutifully went along with it for several years.

'Rest' in music actually represents no music at all. Silence. Nothing. It even has several music notation symbols to represent it. It can happen pretty much anywhere and last for short or long periods. When I was learning music notation I didn't really appreciate rests much. I was usually speeding through a (to me dull) song on the violin just trying to reach the end of it as soon as possible. However, when I began composing songs I saw the true power of the rest. It can be very powerful when used in the right place for the right duration. This pause in play can convey the true emotion of a song and is as vital in composition as the notes themselves. They are the ying and yang of songwriting. Imagine someone delivering a speech with no pauses. It would be a monotonous delivery that would soon lack effect as the audience gradually zoned out.

Rests in music often aren't even noticed but next time you listen to a song try and spot them and you'll begin to see their value. They pop up in many songs. One of my favourite examples of a rest is in Prince's *Purple Rain*. It's short but has a lot of impact. He builds the emotion through the verse then stops all the instruments dead before continuing the lyrics at the start of the chorus ahead of the instruments being brought back in with a wham.

What I'd like you to bookmark in your memory is that a rest doesn't just happen randomly – it is deliberate. A decision made by the songwriter. A purposeful choice. An effort to maintain and focus our attention on the song. In this same way we should ensure that we deliberately place rest/s in our daily lives. Not just sleep (we'll get to that later in this chapter) but also periods of deliberate and high quality rest that we purposefully place into our daily existence without guilt.

The word 'deliberate' is important. You may have heard of the 10,000 hour rule. Malcolm Gladwell in his book *Outliers* highlighted the research of Anders Ericsson and heralded this number as the magic formula for truly mastering a skill. However, as often happens this information has been misrepresented over the years across media channels and reproductions of the information. It's not the number of hours of practice that counts but the amount of deliberate and focused high quality practice that delivers results.

Definitions of rest often describe it as a period of inactivity. But this doesn't always have to be the case. Going for a walk or cycling or a swim in the sea can be equally restful to the mind. Periods of tranquility, away from the stresses of work, give our body and brain the time to recharge. Alex Soojing-Kim Pang, in his excellent book titled *Rest*, tells us of many successful names who all deliberately placed periods of rest within their daily routines. Churchill hardly went a day without his afternoon nap, even during the Blitz bombings. He knew how important these breaks were in keeping him functioning to full cognitive capacity during stressful times. Other names such as Steve Jobs, Darwin, Dickens, Stephen King, Tolkien, Haruki Murakami, Salvador Dali and many others enjoyed real breaks throughout their days. Whether through catching brief afternoon naps or walks or yoga or reading. What's noticeable from this list is that it includes names from politics, business, technology, art and literature. Rest offers universal benefits to everyone and is an essential part of effective human functioning.

Later in this chapter I'll explain how music can very effectively and efficiently help us to achieve periods of rest within our busy lives. But first let's look at rest in more detail.

Rest in the modern world

We live in a world where rest seems to have become under appreciated. In the work arena it's often been seen as wasteful, a weakness, irresponsible and even lazy. Overworking in contrast has become admired. Workers who leave the office at 5pm without fail are often criticised and mocked behind the scenes. I've witnessed it on many occasions. The hospitality industry is especially poor in this regard. Staff are expected to stay and extend their hours if they are needed. Lieu hours build up (instead of overtime pay) and can never be recouped due to the ongoing shortage of staff in many workplaces. This is a dangerous trend. We can see already how these sorts of approaches have not resulted in quality of health and wellbeing. Cutbacks since the financial crisis have placed immense pressures on workers. Corporations trying to show a profit cut back on staff wherever they can. Workers today seem to be delivering a workload that in previous years would have been the responsibility of several members of the team. These practices are damaging workforces around the world and resulting in a miserable existence for the millions of employees who suffer within these unhealthy working cultures.

Technology was meant to give us greater periods of rest by delivering more efficient automated solutions that freed us from time consuming daily chores. Cars, computers, washing machines, dishwashers etc. But those machines have instead given us more available hours to spend at the office; check our emails; monitor the movements of our friends on social media; keep abreast of the 24 hour news updates and the weather. I recently downloaded an app that enabled me to monitor how many times I had picked up my iphone during the day. It was rather depressing. I consider myself a fairly light user of social media and not a slave to my emails but the app told me otherwise. It's become a habit. One I need to break. Immediately. So I'm glad that I've been given the chance to write this chapter about the importance of rest, relaxation and sleep because it will remind me to reposition it again in my own daily life.

Burnout in modern working life is reaching epidemic proportions. It's even itemised in the World Health Organisation's international classification of diseases. It's described in that list as "a state of vital exhaustion". According to the Health and Safety Executive (HSE), 526,000 workers in the UK suffered from work-related stress, depression or anxiety in 2016/7, and 12.5 million working days were lost as a result over that period. Up from 11.7 million days in 2015/6.

Psychologists Rachel Andrew and Brian Rock list five signs that people suffering from or heading towards burnout might experience:

- A feeling of exhaustion and lack of energy for anything, flu-like symptoms and disturbed sleep
- Difficulty concentrating, zoning out and going into a daze for hours on end
- Feelings of irritation, frustration and self-criticism
- Feeling overwhelmed by busy places such as supermarkets where the lights are too bright and there's too much noise
- You feel detached from things you used to love

This isn't just a UK problem. Several studies and articles examining the American workplace have described occupational stress as 'rampant' and saturating USA businesses. The Huffington Post said "the American workplace is broken". Unhealthy work practices and cultures have created an environment which has diminishing returns. According to an estimate by researchers at Harvard and Stanford University workplace stress creates up to $190 billion worth of additional healthcare costs per year. This is due to the overwork culture that we have created.

Many countries in the developed world appear to have dug a hole and everyone is now disappearing down it. We need to completely rethink the way in which we reward employees. Currently overwork is praised and rewarded and when you have some people in teams who practice overwork everyone else is compelled to try and match them. It becomes a race to hell. Overwork needs to be re-evaluated. Effective work over shorter hours needs to be championed in workplaces. A working environment where employees don't feel they can take lunch breaks or holidays because their workload is too great is a working environment that will ultimately fail. Because it's quite simply unsustainable. Humans will either leave (meaning that the company's investment in them over previous years would be wasted) or they will have to take time off work to recover from illness brought on by occupational stress. Either way the business loses and so does the employee. So a radical rethink is required - immediately.

In January 2017 the French government introduced new legislation giving workers in the country "the right to disconnect'. A study by Technologia, a specialist in occupational health, stated that 3.2 million workers (12% of the French workplace) are at risk of burnout. The social cost of this is estimated to be €2.5 billion per year. The new law encourages employers and employees to move away from a culture of "always on" attitudes and to stop sending or checking emails outside of working hours. French owned global telecom company Orange have also introduced their own rules on this topic. Between 2008 and 2009 approximately 19 employees committed suicide. Orange trained managers to realize the pressures that out of work emails place on workers who feel obligated to constantly check emails and reply immediately due to fear of punishment or loss of credibility.

It's also worth noting that these daily stresses are not purely limited to those still within the workplace. They equally apply to those who are unemployed or retired. We are living in a world where stresses of finance and families surround us if we let them.

Why do we need rest and relaxation in addition to sleep?

It's possible to enjoy good quality rest without sleeping but not possible to enjoy good quality sleep without resting. Waking rest is often referred to as relaxation. A waking state where we are free from any perceived anxiety and tension. Sometimes this is linked to recreation and achieved by participating in activities that we find enjoyable and absorbing. Of course it's easy to recommend these periods of rest and relaxation but if your reality is a 10 hour work day followed by a rushed commute to collect the kids from the child minder and then cook dinner and do bath-time and laundry....then when are these periods of rest meant to be fitted in? Modern life is hectic.

According to UK government regulations workers have the right to "one interrupted 20 minute rest during their working day if they work more than 6 hours per day". That break doesn't even have to be paid in certain employment contracts. That 20 minute rest break sounds pretty short but many workers don't even manage to enjoy that. The term 'working lunch' has become commonplace with people munching on sandwiches in front of their computer screens or at lunch meetings with colleagues or clients. It's rare to find workers who regularly leave the office and take proper time out during their working day. Often if they do "pop out" it's to race to the dry cleaners or the bank or post office to run chores.

However, the good news is that these issues are now

receiving regular attention in the media. The current movement in workforce wellbeing is a positive one. Mental health is being openly championed and recognised as essential to happiness and productivity. Corporations are realising that they have a responsibility and appear to be recognising the need for change. We work to earn money to help us live the lives we want to lead. So it's important that the work-life balance should probably be thought of in terms of life-work balance. Where life comes first, not work.

At the time of writing the South Korean government had just announced cutting its working week limit from 68 hours a week to 52. Still a long way off from Germany and Denmark whose workers put in 26 and 27 hours a week respectively, according to the Organisation for Economic Co-operation and Development. British workforces on average work 32 hours per week – 1,676 hours a year. The United States average working hours per year clocks in at 1,783. That's more than 400 hours a year more than workers in Germany - more than 50 days a year extra (based on an 8 hour working day). Mexico tops the table though with 2,255 hours per year.

The Science of Sleep

We spend a third of our life asleep. It's clearly an essential part of effective human functioning. There have been many 'theories of sleep' presented by researchers over the years. Memory consolidation theories of sleep have outlined how the brain uses sleep time to process information gathered throughout the day in order to commit it to long-term memory. The restorative theories of sleep suggest that sleeping is essential for restoring essential physiological and cognitive functions. Scientists have observed how sleep increases the body's rate of cell division and protein synthesis, demonstrating that repair and restoration is significant during this process. More recently researchers have made some important breakthroughs in this 'clean up' activity of the brain. It is now known that waste toxins built up in the brain during the day are flushed out during sleep. Fluids flow within the spaces between neurons in the brain. This process clears out waste products that build up during our waking hours when brain cells are performing normal processing tasks. This is now known to have links with Alzheimer's Disease. People with the disease have noticeable levels of beta-amyloid protein in their brains. It is not yet known whether this protein causes the condition or if it builds up in response to the disease. However, what has been observed in recent studies is that lack of sleep leads to more of this protein in the brain. This is now becoming an area of intense research. While we wait for the scientists to figure out the precise mechanics we would be wise to assume that lack of sleep may be a contributing factor in diminishing brain health. Therefore, we should prioritize getting adequate sleep throughout life.

Our bodies release adenosine molecules throughout our waking day. This is the result of the metabolisation of energy. The levels of adenosine build and eventually trigger the onset of drowsiness. The effects of adenosine have been tested using caffeine. Consumption of caffeine (in a cup of coffee for example) is known to prevent adenosine from binding to certain neurons in the brain, resulting in us feeling more alert and less drowsy. Seratonin and melatonin also play roles in sleep cycles. Melatonin production is light sensitive. So when light increases the production decreases and we eventually wake up. Aside from this chemical homeostasis (balance of chemicals throughout the day) our sleep is also dictated by our natural circadian rhythm. This is our internal biological clock whose rhythm rises and falls throughout the day resulting in periods of alertness and sleep. For most adults the strongest desire for sleep occurs between 2am and 4am and in the afternoon between 1pm and 3pm. This circadian clock is controlled by a group of cells in the hypothalamus in the brain. Sticking to regular sleep times can really help maintain quality sleep. Whereas night shifts and jet lag can really hamper it.

There have been considerable scientific advances in the understanding of our sleep state in recent decades. Many studies have been published regarding both its process and importance. Our sleep state used to be considered a passive affair but now we know much more about what happens to us during sleep. The sleeping person appears inactive but this is not at all accurate. There is certainly a reduction in physical movements and response to external stimuli during this down time but there is a lot going on inside us. Physiological functioning, whilst variable during our waking hours, becomes very regulated during sleep. The physical demands placed on the body are removed. Breathing becomes regular. Heart rate is lowered. Body temperature drops. So does blood pressure. Energy metabolism (calorie demand) is reduced.

The drop by 1-2 degrees in core body temperature is thought to be a contributing factor in inducing sleep. The body is able to require less energy to maintain this lower temperature. Many physiological functions are reduced but there are some that increase during this time. Cell repair and growth are often at their peak during sleep hours.

In contrast the brain is extremely busy. Highly active in fact. Thanks to the extensive work of sleep laboratory research and technological advances we are able to monitor the brain's activity during sleep. There are clear phases that we travel through during our sleep journey.

It's commonly agreed that there are 5 stages of sleep and we cycle through them in approximately 90 minutes. The first four stages are known as non-rapid eye movement and are distinctly different from the final stage when rapid eye movement occurs (REM). More recently experts have combined stages 3 and 4 so some studies refer to three NREM stages followed by the REM stage. Stage 1 is a relatively light stage of sleep. This period is usually short (5-10 minutes typically). Feelings of falling and hallucinations can be quite common in this early stage. It's a transition period when you are still somewhat aware of being awake. During stage 2 that awareness of surroundings reduces, body temperature starts to lower and heart rate and breathing become regular. This stage is thought to last around 20 minutes and can make up approximately 50% of a night's sleep. During stage 3 (NREM stage 3 and 4) the deepest sleep occurs.

Sleepwalking tends to happen in this period. People are less responsive, have relaxed muscles and decreased blood pressure and breathing. This stage is sometimes referred to as delta sleep because of the deep slow delta brain waves that are observed. This is also when growth hormone is released. Finally we enter the rapid eye movement stage (REM) of sleep. The brain is much more active now and dreams occur. Muscles are in their most relaxed state. This stage is thought to be important for learning and memory consolidation.

We cycle through these stages throughout the night but they don't necessarily repeat in the same way. Sometimes durations are longer or shorter and we usually don't return to stage 1 unless we wake up and then drift back to sleep. The REM stage tends to last longer throughout the night as we progress through the cycles.

Using music to help achieve quality sleep and rest

When you consider the conditions that are most likely to result in sleep it's clear that music can help promote this. Previous chapters have discussed how music can help us slow and regulate breathing and heart rate, helping us to achieve a state of relaxation. This is a good starting point. Millions of people around the world experience difficulty in getting to sleep or poor quality sleep. Insomnia attracts a lot of research attention. It's a profitable area. Sales of over the counter sleeping aids in the UK grew from £38.8m in 2009 to £48.7m in 2017. Sleep aids are one of the fastest growing categories in consumer health. Western Europe and North America are the two largest global markets with sales of USD804m and USD785m respectively in 2016. Worldwide sales total USD2.2 billion in 2016 and are expected to grow to USD2.5 billion by 2021. This continued growth is attributed to an increasingly stressed and sleepless consumer base. This seems like a large figure but it falls way below the largest over the counter category (cough, cold and allergy remedies) that achieved global sales of USD33 billion in 2016. There is a clear trend in Western Europe that shows consumers moving towards herbal options. Whereas consumers in North America tend to still choose chemically-based products.

Music is probably one of the healthiest sleep aids on the market. It's non-chemical, non-invasive and produces no unwanted side effects. What more could you ask for? Finding the most effective music is partly science based and partly a matter of taste. There are endless lists of music for relaxation products on the market. A mass market of relaxation soundtracks. I realise that these soundtracks work for many people otherwise they wouldn't be selling them. However, I must confess they are not for me. I'm much more drawn to some of the work that is being developed by composers such as Max Richter, music duo Silence & Air, Marconi Union and DJ Tom Middleton. All of whom happen to be British based musicians. Their work avoids the usual clichés of relaxation tracks (no dolphins that I can recall but maybe I was asleep) and focuses on great ambient music. It's great that composers have started to move into this field. I think this is going to be a huge growth area.

Weightless by Marconi Union was originally released in 2011 as an 8 minute track. This was a collaboration with the British Academy of Sound Therapy. It has since been described as the world's most relaxing song. It actually charted in the Billboard 100 in January 2017. This British ambient band, formed whilst working in a Manchester record shop in 2003, specifically attempted to use scientific theory to achieve this effect. The goal was to lower heart rate, stress levels and blood pressure. They worked with a sound therapist to fully understand the process. The result is a peaceful production that is so effective it comes with a warning – do not listen while driving. According to tests by Mindlab International the song induced a 65% reduction in anxiety and a 35% reduction in usual physiological rates. Its effectiveness is due to the fact that it followed some key rules that are thought to correlate with relaxation. The song has a rhythm equivalent to 60 beats per minute. The listener's heart rate automatically slows to match this beat. Lyz Cooper, the founder of the British Academy of Sound Therapy, explains that this process (known as entrainment) takes around 5 minutes. It's also important that the song has no repeating melody. A repeating melody is what has made many pop and rock stars very rich. But in this environment it's detrimental to the sleep process. Our brain tends to try and predict what's coming next. Using a melody that has no hooks or repetitive notes helps ensure that the brain switches off. This composition won the Time Magazine Invention of the Year. Impressive. The full length extended version of Weightless is now 10 hours.

In 2015 Max Richter stepped into the insomnia and relaxation limelight with his 8 hour composition titled *Sleep*. A classical piece featuring strings and peaceful piano described by Richter as "a personal lullaby for a frenetic world – a manifesto for a slower pace of existence." Richter cites sleep as an important part of his life, one of his favourite activities and integral to his creativity. Richter did not specifically set out to create a song to sleep to (although his title suggests it) but he mostly just wanted to help people slow down and rest. This was not part of a scientific study but the results are impressive. The live performance in 2015 took place in a concert hall full of hundreds of beds in Berlin. The 8 hour performance started at midnight and ended at 8am. How many people do you think actually heard the whole performance?

In contrast the music duo Silence & Air specifically set out to create a piece of music that triggered relaxation, rest and sleep. Their release titled *Zero Point* in 2017 was spurred by personal problems with insomnia, depression and anxiety. Jake Warren and Andy Gbormittah (aka Silence & Air) used sounds and techniques in this 9 minute piece that are thought to be most effective at focusing the brain from sleep distractions such as wandering thoughts, anxiety, negative emotions. The song also incorporates birdsong and lapping waves but somehow in a manner where I don't feel I'm in a treatment room in a spa. They have purposefully used a series of perfect fifths (technical music term for an arrangement of particular notes) that the human ear is known to find harmonious. The song also contains an element of white noise. This is an invisible attempt to keep us focused on the song and to block out any other unwanted sounds such as traffic. The result is a lovely peaceful piece of music.

An interesting venture called The Sync Project had been making some really interesting waves in music and health research in recent years, especially in the field of sleep. Their Unwind.ai app was released in 2017 and was a personalized music experiment to help you sleep better. The app, when downloaded onto your smartphone, measured your heart rate and then used the heart rate as an input to select and monitor the music. The company was bought by Bose in early 2018 and since then there has been little activity. Hopefully they are busy behind the scenes planning bigger and greater things with their new owner.

DJ Tom Middleton went a step further and actually trained as a sleep coach in 2018 in order to fully understand the cognitive neuroscience and write the perfect song (titled *Sleep Better*) to give us a good night's sleep. "Through my years of touring I've suffered from insomnia myself. I felt I could bring my electronic music, re-think what I was already doing intuitively, and then use science to create soundscapes that actually relax you."

How does music help us sleep?

Music is known to directly affect our autonomic nervous system (ANS). We have already seen examples of this in previous chapters. The ANS controls many body functions (such as breathing, heart rate, digestion and muscular contractions of internal organs) without us consciously having to think about them. The ANS has two divisions: the sympathetic system which is responsible for stimulating and the parasympathetic which is responsible for inhibiting. A bit like an accelerator pedal and a brake pedal. Scientists agree that music can be used to directly stimulate our parasympathetic nervous system. Consequently it can slow our heart rate and breathing. This helps put us into an appropriate state to induce the sleep cycle.

The perils of sleep deprivation

We've already discussed the potential link between lack of sleep and Alzheimer's Disease earlier in this chapter but there are many more detrimental effects of prolonged periods of sleep deprivation. Weight gain, impaired mental performance, increased risk of depression (those already suffering from depression are also likely to suffer from insomnia), increased risk of heart disease, digestive issues, hormone imbalance, decreased physical performance, weakened immune system, accelerated tumour growth and body aches.

So you can see how vital sleep is to the healthy functioning of the human body. Sometimes people brag about only "needing" 5 or 6 hours of sleep a night. They are literally putting their body under unnecessary pressure. The agreed rules regarding sleep is that adults need 7-8 hours of good quality sleep per night. If you are consistently getting less sleep than that you are simply building up a sleep debt and the effects may not be immediately apparent. Give sleep and rest the respect it deserves. Sleep is not a weakness, it's a strength.

HOW DO I APPLY THIS IN LIFE?

In Daily Life

Taste dictates results according to my experience. So it's important to try different styles of music until you find what works for you. There will be a song or type of song that works so don't give up. It might be classical or it might be one of the relaxation songs mentioned above or it might be one of the relaxation albums featuring dolphins (just because they don't work for me doesn't mean they won't work for you) or it might be Enya or the soft-rock ballads of the 1980s. Persevere until you unlock the answer.

Find music that has a slow, steady rhythm (of 50-60 beats per minute if possible). You might find that *Wish You Were Here* by Pink Floyd does the trick in terms of winding down at night. But for some people they prefer calmer instrumental music with less emotion. Vocals in music can sometimes be too distracting. But again it's a personal preference so just experiment a little until you find the magic formula that suits you.

It's also very helpful to do as much as possible to achieve the right environment for sleep. Make sure throughout the day you have been using energy through work and/or exercise. Eat healthily throughout the day and take in plenty of water. Avoid your smartphone in the evening as it emits blue light that can fire up the brain and stop you drifting off. Make sure your bedroom isn't too hot (or too cold). Dim the lights in the evening. Listen to chilled out music and read a book in the evening instead of sitting staring at the television. Don't eat too late and avoid caffeine and alcohol. Make sure your bed and pillows are comfortable and wear loose clothing.

Then take your music device to your bedroom, turn out the lights and drift off. Make sure the volume isn't too loud. At night in silence you will need it at a very low setting. You'll still be able to hear it. Set a timer if you can so that it switches off and doesn't wake you up later in the night.

Do the opposite in the morning to help wake up. Set your alarm so that the music gently wakes you up. Bill Withers' *Lovely Day* is a popular choice as it starts quite gently and builds into a nice, upbeat, recognizable melody. Throw open the curtains and open the window. Start the day with a great breakfast.

In Business

Although sleep typically happens in the home time of your employees it's still vital to your business that you ensure they get enough of it. So help them to understand the importance of sleep.

Hire a sleep coach and run some sessions to help people understand the principles so they can get the best quality sleep.

As we discussed earlier in this chapter rest during the day is as important as a good night's sleep. Encourage walking meetings instead of spending hours inside meeting rooms or at desks. You'll be surprised at how much can get achieved just by talking whilst walking - away from powerpoint presentations and trays of biscuits.

Urge workers to take proper lunch breaks. These working lunches in front of computers should be banned in my opinion. They are part of an unhealthy culture that is both unnecessary and damaging. Nurture a culture where workers don't feel guilty if they go and sit in the local park or square to read the paper or listen to music and enjoy a real break. Champion people who put quality rest into their working day.

If you have space for it maybe create a low light chillout room for reading, napping, yoga or mindfulness. Put some headphones in there and a device that people can use to connect to a streaming service like Spotify. Many workers might be embarrassed to go in there at first so you'll need to run some sessions in the early days to help this room become somewhere that people feel they can comfortably spend time in without feeling like an idiot.

Sleep is essential to a fresh, energetic and successful business.

6. GOOD TIMES
The social impact of music as we age

The recently retired segment of the population grew up with rock, pop and punk. They are unlike any previous generation of pensioner. They have completely different memories, experiences, attitudes and tastes. This chapter examines the health effects of social activity and explores how music can be used to maintain health throughout retirement by bringing people together socially.

The population of nations used to be described as pyramid-shaped. It was an appropriate term to describe how the majority of people were in the lower age groups, with the numbers gradually reducing with age, due to increasing morbidity. The top of the pyramid was the narrowest point with just a small percentage of the overall population living to 80+ ages.

Today it's common for people to live into their 80s. In

fact, the Office for National Statistics in the UK now even has a 100+ category to cater for the increasing number of centenarians. For many years those reaching their 100th birthday would automatically receive a congratulatory note from the Queen. Now these birthdays are becoming so frequent that if you want a card it's necessary to actually request this congratulatory message from Her Majesty by completing an online application form. They are also sent out for 105th birthdays, but no longer for the years in between. These birthdays have become too numerous.

According to the Office of National Statistics people are living longer than ever before but with a growing number of long-term chronic conditions - diabetes, heart disease and dementia. By the age of 65, it is reported that people are likely to have at least one of these illnesses. By 75 it is likely they will have two. Over the next 20 years research by the Institute for Ageing at the University of Newcastle forecasts a 179% increase in the number of people of pension age being diagnosed with cancer, and a 118% rise in diabetes. The Institute for Fiscal Studies estimates that the average 65-year-old in the UK costs the NHS 2.5 times more than the average 30-year-old. An 85-year-old costs more than 5 times as much. The IFS believes over the 10 years to 2020, the NHS budget across the UK will not have increased enough to keep pace with the ageing and growing population. There are 850,000 people with dementia in the UK, with numbers set to rise to over 1 million by 2025. This will soar to 2 million by 2051. 70% of people in care homes have dementia or severe memory problems. For every person living with dementia, the annual cost to the UK economy is over £30,000.

Scientists are focused on understanding the ageing process, hoping this knowledge will eventually give them the power to slow or stall it. The current life expectancy in the UK has risen from 65 to 81 years as medical advances help people survive the heart disease, strokes and cancers that would have killed our ancestors. Scientists at Newcastle University have identified for the first time the mitochondrial complex that causes skin ageing. Researchers in California are trialling blood transfusions by giving older participants blood from younger healthy individuals. The Ageing Research department at King's College London is examining the anti-ageing properties in Indian spices and tea. Gene editing could in future give us the ability to keep cells healthy to stop illnesses from ever coming into being. According to Transparency Market Research the anti-ageing market will be worth £151 billion worldwide by 2019. With a market of this size and value it's almost inevitable that scientists and pharmaceutical companies will continue to explore this field until they find solutions. Living to 100 years old or longer could become the new norm in the near future.

We're getting older, but we're also getting lonelier. Research shows that loneliness and social isolation are harmful to our health. According to the World Health Organisation a prolonged reduction in social connections is as great a risk factor for early death as smoking 15 cigarettes a day, and is worse for us than well-known risk factors such as obesity and physical inactivity. Loneliness increases the likelihood of mortality by 26%.

Loneliness and social isolation in the United Kingdom

- 17% of older people are in contact with family, friends and neighbours less than once a week and 11% are in contact less than once a month (Victor et al, 2003)
- Over half (51%) of all people aged 75 and over live alone (ONS, 2010)
- Two fifths of all older people (about 3.9 million) say the television is their main company (Age UK, 2014)
- 63% of adults aged 52 or over who have been widowed, and 51% of the same group who are separated or divorced, report feeling lonely some of the time or often (Beaumont, 2013)
- 59% of adults aged over 52 who report poor health say they feel lonely some of the time or often, compared to 21% who say they are in excellent health (Beaumont, 2013)
- A higher percentage of women than men report feeling lonely some of the time or often (Beaumont, 2013)

The World Health Organisation emphasises the seriousness of loneliness, which they say is becoming "a modern epidemic". WHO urges practitioners to nurture more opportunities for social participation, especially with younger generations, in order to combat isolation among older residents. We need to bring people together regularly in social settings to forge new and wider local networks, which in turn keeps people off their sofas.

Cities in particular need to address this growing epidemic of loneliness and ensure that their urban planning provides plenty of opportunity for residents of all ages to access and enjoy music. For example, Mayor of London, Sadiq Khan's new London Plan lists and protects music venues and street performance as 'assets'. This is the first time this official recognition has been given to this sort of music infrastructure.

Although loneliness and isolation are connected they are separate concepts. Loneliness is a subjective state with a number of forms. For example, someone who lacks a social network or a broad group of friends, neighbours or colleagues experiences social loneliness. Whereas someone who lacks a significant other with whom a close emotional attachment is formed experiences emotional loneliness. Loneliness can be a chronic condition throughout life which is exacerbated with age or an acute condition which suddenly flares up in later life in response to life changes such as bereavement. So how can music help in these situations?

Today's retired population grew up in music venues. Many of them met their partners in local music venues. According to *The Economist*, in 1953 dance halls were the UK's second biggest entertainment industry after cinema. They attracted approximately 200 million dance hall visitors per year compared with 90 million spectators at football matches. However, the popularity started to subside by the end of the 1960s as new styles of music took over. Some dance halls morphed into bingo halls, some into cinemas, some into nightclubs, many were demolished. Live music venues took over as the new places to be. By the 1970s and 80s the ever-evolving music styles drove the entertainment establishments, and the remaining dance halls morphed into nightclubs. However, it was still possible to hear live music at the local pub and they remained an important social venue for local communities. But pubs and music venues have been disappearing at an alarming rate. Between 2011-2016 the number of town centre pubs, bars and nightclubs fell by approximately 2,000 in the UK. Whereas cafes, restaurants and fast food establishments grew by approximately 6,000. As a result, opportunities for older people to connect with the music of their youth are dwindling.

Small local music venues continue to adhere to the traditional live music model - targeting the youth market. There is no concerted effort to try and draw in the local audience aged 40-75+. It means the local venues are missing out on the cash in the pockets of the 40+ aged population. But more importantly, these venues could act as important hubs for this older demographic and therefore play a role in ensuring the population remains socially active throughout life.

Public spaces can also play a vital role in improving social cohesion in communities. Our squares, parks and streets often provide perfect locations for music based performances and events. Whether it's an organised series of brass bands in a bandstand or a street performer busking in the high street music can make public places much more vibrant and appealing places to spend time.

It's a highly effective placemaking tool. Visits to the local shops might sometimes be the most social engagement that socially isolated people have in their lives. Street performance is a particularly interesting model. It provides important access to live music, especially for those who can't afford it or feel too intimidated to go to music venues alone. It's possible for people who live alone to come into their high streets and sit and enjoy live music. There are no barriers for them to cross. It's much easier to enjoy a performance by a talented busker on the street than go to a venue for the first time on your own. The abundance of coffee shops on the high street also makes it possible to sit and enjoy a cuppa whilst taking in the performance nearby. Buskers are often the first taste that children experience of live music. Watch their faces light up next time you see a child spot a busker. They often insist on staying to watch and dance. We are drawn to music from birth. The role of music in creating vibrant public spaces is something that has received growing attention in the past few years. Especially in cities. I have been working increasingly in this field.

In 2017 I ran a 12-month case study in a town on the south coast of England called Folkestone. I wanted to take the principles that we had been working on for the Mayor of London and test whether they could be applied in a smaller urban setting. Using live music performances outdoors as the tool to drive social cohesion, economic development and health. This seaside town of 50,000 people has seen a notable decline in the average number of people in each household, and it's expected to see a very significant ageing of the local population in coming years to 2026 (it's already older than the UK average). This will have implications for the health and care requirements. There is a serious healthcare crisis of epic proportions looming in this district if the skewed population cannot be rebalanced by attracting and retaining younger age groups aged 18 to 40 years old who have been leaving the town. Central Folkestone has particularly low social capital (a lack of social networks amongst residents). The challenge is to develop the district using social resources in a way that all people can share in. Unemployment is higher than national average and earnings are below regional levels. Folkestone has severe areas of deprivation compared with other areas in the region. The areas of significant socio-economic disadvantage are often in very close proximity to affluent neighbourhoods. Education and skills development are also low with fewer people holding a degree level qualification than anywhere in the UK.

In the last decade the town has committed significant resources to visual arts and culture and this has resulted in the regeneration of an area of run-down properties in the harbour area into a 'Creative Quarter'. However, this predominantly high culture content has not succeeded in engaging the disadvantaged population as they do not identify with it. It does not match their cultural tastes. There have been 2 murders in the past 2 years (both within the Creative Quarter area or nearby) and the regenerated park in the heart of this neighbourhood has become recognised as a location where gangs and drug dealers base their activity.

The primary initial focus of the overarching case study, titled *Folkestone Music Town*, tested the use of popular music and themes in creating social opportunities for older adults – preferably within multi-generational settings rather than through "Over 50s"-type events. Popular music themes were used to match the taste preferences of the target demographic and broader. I hoped to see increased participation by residents of all ages (across all socio-economic groups) at existing local music venues, and through new use of outdoor spaces and venues to create additional music themed social opportunities. This activity fell into the 3 sub-projects below.

SURROUND SOUNDS
Monthly music talks and social get-togethers

We launched a series of popular music themed monthly talks and social gatherings called Surround Sounds at local venues. The format encouraged people to bring the first records they ever bought (if they still owned them) and to talk about their early music memories and experiences. We featured music themed talks and quiz games. These 3 monthly events showed the potential that heritage music themes and talks can bring to the table. Multiple generations came. Some of the older attendees had never stepped inside the music venue before although it has been in the town for 20 years. At one event we discovered that two people had been at the same music concert in the 1980s despite being 20 years apart in age. On one occasion we connected live via Skype to a guest speaker in Los Angeles to discuss the career and influence of Chuck Berry to mark his recent passing. The ages of attendees ranged from 16 to 84 years old.

THE ROOFTOP DISCO
Social get-together

We created a new weekly daytime outdoor disco in Folkestone to celebrate the 40th anniversary of when legendary New York City discotheque Studio 54 started. We located it on the rooftop of the local large scale (1,800 capacity) music venue that was established 90 years ago. The rooftop has direct views of the sea and on a clear day you can see France. However, this spectacular terrace is very rarely used for events. It's a prime location. The music repertoire was exclusively classic 1970s and '80s disco hits. This genre seems to succeed in pulling several generations onto dance floors at weddings. Despite our minimal marketing and production budget, the crowd grew week by week. By our final weekend we had an eclectic mix of people on that dance floor – toddlers, war veterans, dementia sufferers, mental health patients, millionaires, homeless individuals and even dogs.

This was one of the most satisfying music events I've ever created – and I've created a lot of crazy events over the decades. It drew people from all walks of life regardless of income, age, class, sexuality, religion, health or ethnic origin. They were dancing for hours, laughing, making new friends, catching up with old friends, enjoying the views, sipping cocktails (not the toddlers!) and eating hot dogs. It visualised the very definition of how music can bring people together.

THE HENDRIX WEEKEND
Celebrating Folkestone's music heritage

The third event format was held in November. We marked the 75th birthday of Jimi Hendrix. This may seem a bit of a curveball but there is a reason. Noel Redding, the bass player in the Jimi Hendrix Experience, was born and grew up in Folkestone. The Jimi Hendrix Experience played one of their earliest gigs at a venue in Folkestone in 1966. Not only did 2017 mark the 75th birthday of Jimi Hendrix but it marked the 50th anniversary of their first album, *Are You Experienced?*, and 25 years since they were inducted into the Rock & Roll Hall of Fame. With the support of several small, independent venues and music enthusiasts in the town we put together a 4-day weekend of Hendrix themed events including gigs, DJs, talks, jam sessions, exhibitions and even a silent disco. At one of our events we connected live with Seattle's Museum of Popular Culture, home of Jimi Hendrix, so we could sing Happy Birthday along with the special guests and Hendrix's family at the official birthday party. This weekend sparked the attention of the local media and successfully attracted local residents of all ages. This was particularly noticeable at the jam session where we had several attendees aged over 50 who hadn't played their guitars for many years.

This 12-month case study was a very simple illustration of

what can be achieved using popular music themes if a community works together. Age barriers were non-existent. But due to a lack of marketing funds the reach was modest. All events were well attended but Folkestone has a higher than average 60+ population. So to really penetrate that demographic it's necessary to achieve more reach. We need to enlist venues around the country to run similar events to these, to help improve social isolation. In turn, it helps the local music ecosystem generate greater revenues. The hardest step is getting new customers out of their front doors and in through the front doors of the venue. Once that hurdle is crossed it's generally much easier to continue to access those older customers. In fact, once they've been through the door – providing they've had a great experience – they often become the venue's biggest fans, promoting their events to friends, family and neighbours.

Social isolation can happen in residential care homes too. You might think that environments such as this are highly social because they house so many people. However, for residents who are confined to bedrooms it can be very lonely. A music initiative in Folkestone called The Musical Walkabout directly tackles this social isolation by taking music performances into residents' bedrooms. These sessions, led by local musician Nina Clark, are hugely popular with the residents and often result in enthusiastic sing-alongs of songs. Within the Folkestone Music Town case-study we approached local care homes and schools to try to create a model of best practice that illustrates how music can effectively connect all corners of communities from birth to death. This is an ongoing process which we hope to complete by the end of 2019, resulting in an extremely comprehensive range of music themed opportunities that successfully engage all local residents and tourists no matter what their age. And ensuring that no-one is socially isolated in the town.

A recent report published by the Arts Council stated that most people within their survey had said that music is something that has improved their quality of life. We must ensure that people have as much access to it as possible in order to maximise the social benefits that it can deliver.

HOW DO I APPLY THIS IN LIFE?

In Daily Life

The first step to making changes is perhaps admitting to yourself that you, or someone you care about, are socially isolated and lonely. There have been several scientific studies that have examined what the typical indicators might be. One study of 2,500 people over 6 years suggested a link between materialism and loneliness. Those who were lonely tended to accumulate more possessions and were keen shoppers. Shopping can help socialise people of course because it gives them the opportunity to spend time in retail locations, unless it's done online from their home.

A series of studies in 2013 also found links between loneliness and people taking regular long hot baths. It was suggested that this sensation of warmth helps comfort the individual. The studies found that feelings of social coldness and disconnectedness were shown to trigger a need for social warmth that can be satisfied instead by applications of physical warmth, as in taking warm baths or showers. Scientists also have found links between loneliness and impaired immunity, meaning that individuals are more likely to suffer from illnesses, especially those caused by viruses. The increase in the stress hormone cortisol also hampers general health and sleep patterns. There have also been studies that have demonstrated a possible link between binge watching television series and loneliness and depression, with viewers using this activity to subconsciously escape from feelings of loneliness.

Are any of these symptoms sounding familiar? Either for you or someone you know? Listening to more music can help regulate cortisol and improve mood. This doesn't necessarily increase social connections on its own, but an enhanced mood can increase the likelihood of someone actually leaving the house and deciding to engage socially. But it may need someone to help them take the first step of going to a new venue for the first time, or to a choir session for example. Once the first visit has been achieved social interactions can start to happen quite quickly after that. Social media is particularly useful in helping people to engage.

Get involved with local music events and venues. Maybe help to organise or promote some events. You can very quickly start to build a social circle if you start to regularly visit a music venue.

In business

If you're in the business of running venues or exercise to music classes or choirs or dance classes - or just in the field of general health and wellbeing – are you reaching people who are socially isolated? Do the regulars in your class know anyone who they think might be socially isolated and who they could bring along with them for a taster session? It's not a conversation that often happens. One of the hardest aspects of socialising lonely and socially isolated people is identifying them and reaching them. Think about what you might be able to do to help reverse someone's loneliness. It can make a big difference and often just takes small steps. Artificial Intelligence, such as the Elli-Q companion bot, and use of technology such as Skype and Facetime to engage with distant family members can help, but face to face human interaction is always preferable.

If you employ people, how do you ensure they are socially healthy? Does your company have regular social events? Are they music based? Do you offer dance lessons or exercise to music classes? Do you have a company choir? What happens to your staff after they retire? Do you have any form of ongoing social club (like University alumni) so that they can continue to easily maintain a social attachment to former colleagues? Think about how you can help maintain the social health of your workforce. Do you know how many of your employees leave work and go home to an empty house? Loneliness can result from a life change, such as starting a family, children leaving home, a relationship break-up, or bereavement. Even career promotions can socially isolate workers by removing them from the social circle they were once part of, especially if the promotion involves a relocation. It's important as a business owner or manager to recognise that loneliness can be present within the workplace as well as at home. Home workers are also particularly prone to loneliness due to the extensive hours spent working alone. So if you have a workforce wellbeing programme, make sure it also addresses loneliness and includes opportunities for enhanced social interaction.

It's not just businesses that this applies to. Officials responsible for towns and cities also need to recognise the importance of social interaction to human wellbeing. Music is a social glue and in a workforce (and general population) that is now increasingly featuring several generations popular music can regularly bring people together for good times. Help nurture as many music based social opportunities as you can. Particularly in outdoor public spaces which are much less intimidating than indoor venues for people to go along to on their own.

7. STAIRWAY TO HEAVEN
The importance of music in later life

According to the World Health Organisation the average life expectancy for someone born in 2016 varies dramatically depending on where you live. In the UK your life expectancy is predicted to be 81 years (79 for males and 83 for females). In the USA it's 78 years. In Nigeria it's 55 years. That's a shocking insight into the gap that still exists between countries across the world in terms of poverty and health. However, it's important to remember that even within countries those disparities and inequalities also exist. In the UK you are more likely to live longer if you are born in Richmond, London than in Blackpool for example. Widening economic inequality in the USA is also driving inequalities in health care. Wealthy Americans are now expected to live longer than poor Americans by 10-15 years according to a report in *The Lancet* in 2017. In the USA this is partly due to the fact that the poorest cannot afford health insurance. Whereas in the UK the National Health Service provides medical assistance to everyone equally. Yet these health inequalities still exist in Britain too. So our general choices throughout life clearly also play a key role in our life expectancy.

Our healthy life expectancy – the number of years we spend in good health – has not been increasing in line with our life expectancy. So the good news is that you will probably live longer, the bad news is that you may not enjoy it. Less than a century ago people commonly died from infectious diseases following a relatively short bout of ill health. Medical science advances have helped us to control, and in some cases eradicate, these diseases. Now we die from chronic illnesses caused by our lifestyles, often with long periods of moderate to severe ill health. The increase in life expectancy and the number of years retirees now spend in poor health has made the original pension fund and NHS models unsustainable. The first "old age" pension in the UK was introduced in 1908. Men aged 70 would receive five shillings a week (about £14 today). This was in an era where average life expectancy was 47! A century later and the wheels fell off the pension system. The underestimation of life expectancy increases and the overestimation of pension fund investment returns made the current model unviable. This is a mess of epic proportions. Most people are going to have to continue working well into their 70s in future years. The NHS has also buckled under the weight of the problem. This problem isn't just a UK one. At the time of writing the Russian Government had just announced that the pensionable age would be raised to 65 for men. This has caused uproar due to the fact that 43% of the male population are likely to not live that long, according to life expectancy figures that haven't changed in the past 50 years.

Our lifestyle choices are made earlier in life but even in later life there are choices you can make that can increase your chances of extending your healthy life expectancy. The prominently advertised ones of course relate to diet and exercise. Eat sensibly and exercise often. But as most people chose not to do that earlier in life are they really going to be able to motivate themselves to do it when they retire? (we discussed this problem in chapter 1) This is why music can be pivotal in later life. It's an enjoyable vehicle that delivers health benefits. Don't wait until you're diagnosed with diabetes, dementia, arthritis or any other chronic illness. Start now. Dance more, sing more, get out with friends and enjoy more live music events, learn an instrument, write a song, listen to more music on a daily basis. Revisit the music soundtrack of your life on YouTube. The amount of amazing video content of iconic music moments is incredible. Whether you're looking for Gracie Fields entertaining the troops in 1939 or The Beatles' legendary performance at Shea Stadium in 1965 I guarantee you will find it on YouTube.

A few years ago I was invited to deliver a music workshop for 45 guests aged 65+ at City Hall in London. It was part of the annual Silver Sunday campaign in the UK tackling loneliness in older age. I decided to show the group how to use YouTube. Most of them had never used it before although they all had computers. I showed them how simple it was to access, and asked them for some of their favourite music memories. Then we watched Elvis on *The Ed Sullivan Show*, The Rolling Stones on *Ready Steady Go*, and Dusty Springfield's television show. They were amazed. At the end of the day I saw some of them outside as we were all leaving. They enthusiastically told me that my session was their favourite of the afternoon (the other workshops included the English National Opera, National Theatre, Sadler's Wells for example). I believed them. Hopefully they continued to play with YouTube when they got home. You should too. Don't sit in front of uninspiring daytime television. Start searching the amazing music archives on the internet.

Music and Dementia

Music offers unique results for those who have been diagnosed with dementia. It's often the only thing that successfully unlocks those who are shut down in the later stages of this illness. It's much easier to ease a dementia sufferer into a dance environment, singing environment or performing environment if they had been actively participating before they developed the condition. Hence, it's important to start this routine when you are in good health. As well as playing a preventative role music engagement may pay dividends in future years if you are diagnosed with a terminal neurological condition.

My first experience of dementia was seeing our neighbour,

who was in her 70s, cutting the grass in her garden. This wouldn't have seemed out of the ordinary but for the fact she was wearing her underwear over her clothes. She had no family locally and was eventually moved to the local care home further along our road. Almost 40 years later, I now have 3 family members aged 70+ who are experiencing various stages of dementia, and one friend and former colleague who was diagnosed with early onset Alzheimer's in her early 50s.

Worldwide, the WHO predicts the number of people with dementia is expected to increase to 75 million in 2030 and 132 million in 2050.

There has been much work in the field of music and dementia over many years. It's not a new discovery that music can bring many positive effects to those with dementia. It has long been evident that music can help people with dementia connect with people and express emotions. It can be used to calm them if they become agitated. It can reduce social isolation and facilitate exercise. Just like it does in people who do not have dementia in fact.

When I was at primary school in the 1970s I would regularly sing in local care homes. I remember the staff would regularly be singing too. It's a simple thing that can make a huge difference in terms of the amount of musical experiences and social experiences that residents benefit from. It's also hugely cost effective.

When people find out that I work in the music industry

they often tell me that they "can't sing a note". This is something we need to get over. Let's break down social awkwardness in the general public and give everyone permission to sing again. Quality isn't necessarily important, it's the taking part that counts. This is the same problem we discussed previously where people are too embarrassed to dance. These singing and dancing activities tend to be more likely after people have had a few drinks. They are more relaxed. Ideally we need to be able to arrive at that state without needing alcohol.

We know through decades of scientific evidence that music can deliver positive health benefits. I was using music to control anxiety and manipulate mood state in Olympic athletes in the 1990s. There was a solid body of existing research on the effects of music on the brain even then. Positive benefits can be achieved even just through the simplest measures of turning on a radio and listening to almost any music. People do not necessarily need 'expert' qualifications or any scientific knowledge to do the simplest steps. Anyone can deliver basic and positive experiences using music. This is how to ensure that the maximum number of people do so.

Training is not an essential element. I witnessed how this approach failed in the fitness industry. In the 1990s the industry was successfully convincing people that they needed 'prescribed' fitness programmes and personal trainers and gym inductions in order to get fit and healthy. This misguided perception created a barrier. A lot of people couldn't afford personal trainers and were afraid of doing exercises themselves in case they were doing it wrong and causing damage. In reality the damage caused by not doing any exercise over a lifetime outweighs the potential damage you may incur by doing a press up incorrectly. Now the situation is so desperate regarding the health of the nation that the government has had to drop the bar to the lowest entry point to try and encourage activity. The latest public health advertising campaign on the London Underground is simply telling people to stand up more often!

Delivering high quality music intervention led by highly trained professionals in music therapy is an excellent proposal. But in today's economic landscape it's not always a viable proposition due to the cost of achieving this. Empowering ordinary individuals and educating care home owners is the only way of reaching the masses to ensure that:

a) those with dementia enjoy music regularly

b) those who don't yet have dementia are using music in their everyday lives so as to enjoy the preventative benefits and help maintain brain health.

At a time when funding is scarce what's needed is a solid PR campaign to encourage the general public to take steps to get more music in their lives so that more people benefit from these already proven effects. A joined up campaign that encourages them to join local choirs, attend more live music events at local venues, learn instruments, dance more, socialise more would have dramatic effects in terms of engagement and the consequent health benefits. A single campaign that all related organisations can collaborate on to extend the reach of that single message could be a gamechanger.

We work closely with the Musicians' Union, PRS for Music, PPL, Featured Artist Coalition, and the Music Managers Forum. Across these UK music industry bodies they have phenomenal reach in terms of accessing musicians in local communities across the UK. This gives access to tens of thousands of musicians that could be relatively easily harnessed by local care homes and families of those diagnosed with dementia. We regularly connect local musicians with local care homes and the effects are instant and excellent. Care staff who work in care homes and hospitals need specialist training. Musicians coming in to deliver live performances do not. In fact, they do not even need to be highly skilled musicians. Many popular hits of the 1950s and 1960s can be played with just a few major chords on a guitar. These are the songs that the care home residents of today grew up with.

The existing music ecosystem in local communities is not being fully harnessed for health, especially for the older population. For example, there are venues in each town and city that can become social hubs for the community. Providing a safe place for choirs, music lessons, discos, live music performances. We have been presenting this concept at the Venues Day conference for the past 2 years. The Sanctuary night club in Glasgow has recently started running a 'Daytime Disco' on Mondays, welcoming over 50s (including those with dementia) to strut their stuff on the dance floor. We are currently talking with Attitude is Everything to include dementia within their work. This organisation works with music venues in the UK to help them become deaf and disabled friendly spaces. We are adding dementia to their work so that they can also encourage venues to become dementia friendly spaces.

Simplify. Simplify. Simplify. Even just turning on a radio can have a positive effect. We need to encourage staff and families to play a role in delivering music in their own lives and the lives of those they are caring for. We also need to encourage an intergenerational approach so that students and young musicians understand the importance of music throughout life, and are encouraged to create and participate in multi-age music experiences.

The biggest problem that we have at a grassroots level is engaging local GPs and the practice managers. They are not engaged with the local music offering; they do not reply to emails or calls when we try to help connect them. The NHS should make more effort to encourage GP practices and all relevant NHS Trust teams at local level to accept offers of help from the local music ecosystem. I also believe that the positive effects of music should be included in medical training so that the next generation of GPs are much more open-minded and fully understand the capacity of music to deliver positive effects to people's lives. I led the early GP Exercise Referral programmes in the South-East in the 1990s. GPs were very hesitant to have any involvement with local gyms when we started to explore these possibilities. Now it's common practice. People are referred to gyms and fitness centres when they have health problems. Equally, care home business owners should be educated about the value of music so that they build it into their budgets. It can deliver a high return on investment in terms of quality of life. If music was recognized by the CQC as an essential factor in its ratings every care home would ensure they had some level of music provision.

Music and Parkinson's Disease

My grandfather had Parkinson's Disease and died when I was about 7 years old. I don't remember ever hearing him talk. He just used to sit in his chair trembling. Today there is still no cure and medical experts don't know exactly why people develop this progressive neurological condition. We do know that the condition causes the dopamine producing nerve cells to die. As we learnt in previous chapters, dopamine acts as a vehicle, transporting messages to other parts of the brain. So the gradual decline of this chemical in the brain leads to a variety of symptoms such as muscle tremors, slowness of movement, freezing, speech impairment and fatigue.

According to the Parkinson's Association someone in the UK is told they have the disease every hour. 127,000 people in the UK and 1.2 million people across Europe have been diagnosed and currently live with the disease. It's thought that one million Americans are living with Parkinson's at an estimated cost of $25 billion per year. Treatment includes drugs that help to boost dopamine in the brain or replicate its actions. However, as with most drugs there are side effects.

Music on the other hand has been shown to deliver instant results and with no side effects. This non-invasive treatment can help Parkinson's patients as well as those with dementia and is a low risk intervention. In an earlier chapter we learned that the brain responds to music by producing dopamine. People with Parkinson's have a reduced ability to produce dopamine so this has an instantly beneficial effect, especially on motor skills as it assists in the transmission of messages to the motor cortex in the brain.

One of the most high-profile people with Parkinson's is Michael J. Fox. He was diagnosed with the disease in 1991, aged just 29. He was enjoying huge fame at this time due to the recent success of the *Back to the Future* franchise in which he played the lead role Marty McFly. The finale of the first film featured Fox playing a blistering lead guitar solo whilst performing Chuck Berry's hit *Johnny B Goode*. In 2016 Michael J Fox joined Coldplay on stage at their concert at the Met Life Stadium in New York and performed *Johnny B Goode* again. Despite the development of his condition, which has impacted his movement and speech, he is still able to play guitar.

Music can help people with even advanced stage Parkinson's control their movements and walk much more easily. As well as assisting with gait it can also help with speech. Apart from the general fact that music can make people feel happier and increase the quality of life, it can also provide significant physical benefits. Professor Oliver Sacks in an interview details his first experiences with patients who were locked deeply in a Parkinsonian state, unable to move or speak. He described how one elderly patient was a big fan of Chopin and had lived a life filled with music. When they managed to sit her at the piano she would play his 14 minute piece titled 'Opus 49' from start to finish. She was freed temporarily from her Parkinsonian state. However, she didn't even need to actually play the music to also benefit from the same results. If the nursing staff simply said "Opus 49" to her she would mentally perform it in almost perfect timing. At the end of the 14 minutes she noticeably returned to the shut down state that the music in her mind had temporarily freed her from. It is the rhythm of music that lends itself to success as an intervention for patients. The impaired cognitive and motor function seems to be overridden when music is present. This gives patients their tempo back and can help them control movement more effectively. This can greatly improve quality of life from a functional point of view as well as delivering the associated psychological and neurological benefits. Various clinical studies over the years have assessed the impact of music on both motor and non-motor outcomes. There is a clear link between the way that music boosts the production of neurological chemicals and how that in turn can help control symptoms such as difficulty with gait and speech.

Singing is also proven to give positive benefits to those with Parkinson's and there are an increasing number of singing classes and choirs appearing. Sing For Joy was established in London during 2003 when co-founder Nina Temple and a friend were both diagnosed with Parkinson's. They decided that a chronic illness should not mean a life spent in retreat. They decided to form a choir, secured funding from the Parkinson's Disease Society, appointed inspirational jazz singer Carol Grimes as their musical leader, and the highly inventive jazz musician Dorian Ford as their pianist, and they were off. It continues today.

HOW DO I APPLY THIS IN LIFE?

In Daily Life

The previous chapters have given multiple examples of how putting more music in your life throughout life can increase the likelihood of enjoying good health in later years and help prevent the onset of dementia. So make sure you are getting a daily dose of music whatever your age to maximise the likelihood of maintaining brain health in future.

However, if you or a family member have been diagnosed with a progressive degenerative brain disease such as dementia or Parkinson's then you can still benefit immediately from getting more music into daily life. All of the recommendations made in previous chapters still apply equally once you've been diagnosed. Listening to music, playing music, singing, dancing all produce physiological and psychological responses that can improve quality of life. Even in end of life care music can provide a vital link with the individual. In fact it has been found to be one of few stimuli that can successfully reach people in late stage dementia conditions.

As Professor Sacks explained: "Music imprints itself on the brain deeper than any other human experience. Music evokes emotion and emotion can bring with it memory. Music brings back the feeling of life when nothing else can."

Music has exceptionally powerful abilities to stimulate memories and the brain, especially music from one's youth. If you're using music for dementia think about the songs that you or the person you are caring for grew up with. The UK Official Chart website has all the Top 40 charts dating back to the early 1950s. So if you know the person's date of birth it's simple to look up the songs that were the biggest and most popular hits during their teenage years.

I've witnessed sessions whereby people assume that "old people" want to listen to Glenn Miller or Dame Vera Lynn. This is true for people who grew up during the wartime era but for those aged 75 or below they grew up with the explosion of rock and roll and pop rock. It's important to select songs that they can identify with.

In the near future residents of care homes will be demanding Led Zeppelin, Pink Floyd and punk as their song choices. It's important to recognise the popular music era that people grew up with. At the time of writing two men in Germany have hit the news headlines due to their escape from a home for people with cognitive illnesses. They partied in the town of Wacken near the site of the annual heavy metal festival that has been running for almost 30 years. The two men in their late 50s were found by police in the early hours of the morning waiting for a bus back to their home. They were escorted back to their residence. I love their enthusiasm and dedication to partying. I want to live in a world where homes actually organise day trips to music festivals so residents don't have to try and break out!

The old age pensioners of today are the product of decades of popular music exposure. They are different to any previous cohort of old age pensioners. As time goes on each new tranche of care home resident will be more and more aligned with modern music styles and memories. We currently have the 1950s rock and rollers in residence. Closely followed by the fans of the British Invasion pop rock acts of the 1960s. The punk rockers, prog rockers and heavy metal fans are starting to arrive. Then it will be the post punk and new wavers, the goths, the new romantics, the electronic dance music ravers and so on. We need to rethink how we view and treat those in later life. We also need to ensure that those in early childhood continue to enjoy the access to music that their parents and grandparents did. It delivers lifelong benefits from cradle to grave.

In Business

If you're a business owner or manager are you connected at all with care homes in your local area? Do you have a choir that can go and perform for them? Is there a music provision that you can help sponsor? Get in touch with them. Form a link. Let's bring these homes back into the community rather than operating in isolation.

If your business is a care home or residential home what sort of music services are you providing? Are you financially investing in music? Do your residents have radios in their rooms? Do your staff know what radio stations your residents like listening to? Do you have musical instruments available? Do you invite local musicians and choirs into your care home to perform? Do you take your residents out to local music venues or events? Do you encourage your staff to sing? Make music a core part of your business strategy. Take a look at Appendix A where I have outlined some useful information relating to achieving best practice using music.

If you're a local authority are your care homes fully connected to your community or are they isolated? How can you assist in helping them forge connections with the local music community? If you're a musician delivering music services for people with cognitive diseases are you making sure that the song choices match their music memories so you get the best results? When were they teenagers? Check the biggest hits of those years on the UK Official Chart website.

8. THE SCIENTIST
The future of music and health

Throughout this book I've tried to weave in a range of scientific principles, facts, research findings and evidence that help explain the impact that music can have on us. Many of these effects are visible and immediate, some are complex and less obvious. I've tried to keep these facts as simple as possible in previous chapters. This chapter is for those of you who want to look at these principles in a bit more detail and see where the field of music and health seems to be heading. This area has been attracting growing attention over the past ten years. New scientific research facilities and projects have been springing up in academic establishments around the world. There is a thirst for new understanding in terms of the precise ways that music can be harnessed to deliver positive benefits to our body and mind. Technology is now enabling experts to examine this topic in more detail. Here I've selected a few examples of interesting scientific research that's currently going on in the UK, USA and Europe.

The Neuroscientists & Psychologists

For many years I have been following the advances in music and neuroscience research with great interest. The brain is still one of the great mysteries of the world. Much is now known about it's structure and operation but the exact details are still somewhat of a mystery. When discussing music and health the brain is the key ingredient. As we discussed in earlier chapters sound enters our body through our ears (although our bodies can also detect beats and rhythms) and that information is immediately processed by the brain. The effects that happen next are all determined by our brain. So the neuroscience of these processes holds the key for unlocking the precise way that music can deliver health benefits.

According to Darwin's origin of species theory all living creatures share a common ancestry. Apes are our closest relatives and there are clear similarities in DNA and behaviour. Take a look at the video on YouTube of Damian Aspinall returning to Africa to find the gorillas that he bred before re-introducing them to the wild. It's a very touching reunion after 5 years. However, although apes can clearly express emotions and memories they have yet to develop their linguistic skills. Our ability to verbally communicate and develop a vocabulary of sounds (words) that have meaning sets us apart from other living beings.

Humans have larger brains than apes but scientists and linguistic experts believe that it is our musical ability that has been the driver of our advanced language abilities. Experiments have shown that when apes are given the choice between a room with music and a room with no music they choose the room with no music. Neuroscientists have suggested that apes may have some of the neural circuitry that is required for perceiving beats. But as yet they have not found an ape who has rhythm. If you give an ape a drumstick it will probably bang it on an object, but it's unlikely to drum along in time to any music. With the exception of the gorilla in the Cadbury advert who did a fabulous job of drumming to Phil Collins' *In the Air Tonight*. Incidentally that advert is considered one of the most successful of all time. It's won several awards and almost 10 years after it was first aired it was voted as the nation's favourite advert of all time in a poll run by market research company TNS in 2015.

So these unique neural abilities to appreciate and use music have given us several advantages. Our ability to use rhythm, music and dance to communicate and form close communities is unique. These abilities played a key role in developing language and have enabled us to become the dominant species. But where can music take us next? Over the generations it has morphed from being an essential and important part of life and community to becoming mere entertainment. We're surrounded by music in shops, in adverts, it's easier to access than ever before. We previously examined the pressure that music is often placed under in modern society. Now at last, thanks to the efforts of experts and campaign groups, the world is once again realising that as a tool music can deliver many health benefits. The body of scientific evidence is now too large to keep ignoring. The research base continues to grow stronger year after year.

A new lab located at Leiden University in the Netherlands is focusing on specific applications of music to health and well-being. This research, as well as looking at the neural mechanisms of moving to movement, is also examining the impact of music imagery (singing the songs in your head). This centre, called the Music Brain Health Tech (MBHT) Lab, states that "although the application of music to health was long considered non-scientific, its highly prevalent use, together with increasing evidence of replicable neurological responses to music, calls for systematic clinical investigations." Their projects include research examining musically cued movement in rehabilitation contexts, effects of music listening in healthy ageing and dementia, and applications of musical imagery. This clinical focus helps provide extra detail to further convince senior decision makers in health to consider (and deliver) music as an effective health intervention.

The University of Southern California in Los Angeles now has a Brain & Music Program at its Brain and Creativity Institute. Their work has been focusing on the effects of music training on brain development, investigated in terms of psychological (emotional, cognitive, social) and actual neural functions. Music training has been associated with better than average language and mathematic skills and improved hearing and movement but their work aims to identify the mechanism behind these differences. Their ongoing study began in 2012 and follows a group of children who were aged 6 and 7 when the program started. So far the research has provided clear support for the positive impact of music training on brain development. This is evidenced by a greater perception of pitch (improved auditory processing) and improvements in inhibitory function and cognitive skills (such as working memory) evidenced by greater brain activation in the prefrontal region. These findings were published in two scientific journals and stated that as little as two years of music instruction has multiple benefits. It can change both the structure of the brain's white matter (carrying signals through the brain) and grey matter (containing the brain's neurons that process information). Music instruction also boosts the neural networks that are responsible for decision making and the ability to focus attention. The functional MRI scans and EEG readings showed visible changes in the thickness and volume of brain regions. The auditory regions were thicker and the white matter responsible for communicating between the two hemispheres (the corpus callosum) was more robust. "There has been a long suspicion that music practice has a beneficial effect on human behaviour. But this study proves convincingly that the effect is real," said Antonio Damasio, University Professor and director of the Brain and Creativity Institute. Researchers believe that music learning programmes in the community can help children in low socioeconomic status environments. Assal Habibi, assistant research professor of psychology says "we have documented longitudinal changes in the brains of the children receiving music instruction that are distinct from the typical brain changes that children that age would develop. Our findings suggest that musical training is a powerful intervention that could help children mature emotionally and intellectually."

USC has also been investigating the relationship between music and feelings. Their aim is to examine and understand the power of music to elicit a very wide range of emotions. Experiments that enable a close examination of the mechanisms by which the brain processes emotions induced by music will help establish ways in which music can be used as an effective tool for regulating emotions. Thereby, helping individuals to facilitate social behaviour and control mood. Matthew Sachs, a PhD candidate studying neuroscience at USC, published a study completed at Harvard University that measured the body's response to songs. The study found that people who get "the chills' from music actually have structural differences in the brain. They have a higher volume of fibres connecting their auditory cortex to regions of the brain associated with emotional processing. This means the two areas communicate much more effectively. In December 2017 travel brand Airbnb partnered with the USC Brain and Creativity Institute to offer a "Music and Neuroscience" event to the public. The evening featured a range of live music performances and talks from the University's Brain and Creativity Institute.

Nina Kraus, director of the Auditory Neuroscience Laboratory at Northwestern University, is also leading a diverse team of scientists and musicians. Their approach to sound processing has a biological focus and is intent on using the principles of neuroscience to improve human communication, advocating for best practice in education, health and social policy. The work of this laboratory over almost a decade has studied how music shapes the nervous system. Their findings support those of other institutions in the identification of a "musician advantage" for thinking and perceiving due to the neurological changes that occur due to prolonged music learning. As well as examining the effects of music in childhood they also study the effects of ageing on hearing loss. Their research shows that individuals who have participated in music learning in earlier life (particularly childhood) can also reap the benefits in old age. They are more likely to have an improved ability to hear speech in noise. They have superior auditory processing abilities throughout life. This is true even for musicians who have hearing loss in later life. Even these individuals have a greater ability to hear speech in noisy environments because the plasticity (the improved efficient structure of the brain built during music learning) of their brain continues to be greater than that of those who never learnt music. This provides another compelling reason to embed music in childhood experiences. The benefits are lifelong.

Goldsmith's University in London is leading some really innovative research through their Music, Mind & Brain research group and MSc degree. In 2018 they published a study relating to the development of their Music@Home questionnaire as a tool to assess the home musical environment from infancy to pre-school years. It has long been recognised that children under the age of 5 demonstrate enjoyment of singing and engaging with music spontaneously. It is a natural form of expression, especially in early non-verbal years. However, it's still not clear whether the level of musical engagement in these early years contributes to developmental outcomes and gives advantages upon arrival at school as compared with children who have less musical engagement at home in early years. The Goldsmith's team have developed and validated the Music@Home questionnaire to specifically provide a comprehensive psychometric instrument to assess the home musical environment. Their published study included a solid review of the body of research outlining the beneficial effects of formal music experiences on early cognitive, linguistic and social development. These music experiences have referred to those formally delivered in classrooms, not the informal musical experiences they receive in the home as delivered by family members. Other studies have shown the developmental benefits that children experience when growing up in environments where reading and enriched play are frequent. Music, although often within this enriched home learning environment, has never been examined individually. According to their report children's home musical experiences appear to have increased in recent years. This is thought to be related to a combination of increasing technological advancements and sociological changes that have resulted in children spending less time playing outdoors. This new Music@Home questionnaire also assesses parental music experiences and their belief regarding music's effect on development. It provides a comprehensive tool that can now be used in future research to gather more evidence regarding the contribution of the home musical environment to various developmental outcomes. As a Trustee of Young Voices (the largest children's choirs in the world!) I am very interested to see how this questionnaire can be used to gather more evidence to support the importance of music in childhood. Our experience with the Young Voices schools in the UK and USA consistently shows how much of an impact these learning experiences and concerts have on children, teachers and parents. It boosts confidence and motivation and gives performance experiences that they remember for the rest of their lives. This is why these schools sign up again year after year to participate in the Young Voices concert series. Over 1 million children aged 8-11 years old have now performed in a Young Voices concert in the UK. It's a hugely impressive organisation that is filling the serious gap that has emerged as music has been gradually stripped from school curriculums to make way for a targeted focus on STEM subjects (science, technology, engineering, maths) that are deemed more valuable than the arts.

The Computer Scientists

I recently attended a gathering of music neuroscientists in London. The event featured several professors, their graduates and doctoral students. During the 2 days we merely touched on the surface of all the fascinating work that's going on in this field today. However, there were a few examples that really stood out for me. One was a project by a master's student named Pedro Kirk at Goldsmith's University in London. He had created a technological solution to help stroke patients rehabilitate. The principle was quite straightforward but the development of the coding was undoubtedly pretty detailed. In brief, the problem that was being addressed was the rehabilitation of upper limbs in stroke patients. He explained that stroke survivors whose upper limbs are affected often leave hospital having had no rehabilitation at all. As long as they can walk they are discharged. This means that often they are left with lifelong weaknesses in an affected arm. Because the amount of repetitions required to successfully rehabilitate a limb is vast (it was quoted that high dose repetition of up to 500 per session is recommended) people lose energy, focus, interest and consequently rarely complete enough reps to make real progress. Music was introduced as a tool to keep the brain interested and distracted from feelings of fatigue and boredom. These ideas are not new. My own research in the late 1990s used music to increase endurance and delay the onset of perceived fatigue in exercise tasks. However, the innovation in this case was the use of the technology. A computer was connected to a camera. The camera was positioned in front of the patient and could identify the limb that was being targeted. The computer learned the correct movement for that person (for example, correctly bringing the arm forward to pick up a cup from the table). Then when the music was playing during repetitions the computer distorted the sound of the song whenever the arm slightly moved out of the correct position during the movement. A bit like when a radio signal goes a little crackly when it's not tuned in accurately. When the arm movement was corrected the music played perfectly again. This reminded me of a game that was all the rage in the 1970s. You had to carefully move a metal loop along a long coiled line of metal without touching it. Every time the metal connected a buzzer would sound. The idea is simple but if this music and tech intervention can make the task more interesting and therefore help deliver 500 repetitions per session the effects on rehabilitation success would be substantial. Of course at present this type of technology isn't widely available but due to the rapid rate of technology advancement and adoption it soon could be. Most importantly though, 93% of the participants (43 stroke survivors took part in the research) stated that they thought that music helped their rehabilitation and would use it again. There is a clear role for music in neurorehabilitation. The advances in computer technology, machine learning and artificial intelligence over the next five years will have a substantial impact on the scope of health interventions.

Technology company Intuition Robotics has also been working hard in the field of health and artificial intelligence. Their prototype companion robot, Elli-Q, is designed to keep older adults active and engaged. It's not like C3PO, it's a desktop unit without a face. But it has a light display so it can express emotion. Once living with their owner Elli-Q can learn their behaviours and tastes and adapt to them. This enables the device to proactively suggest activities that are most likely to engage the user. For example, asking them if they'd like to play a brain training game with them, or video call their family, or look up some recipes or do some exercises. The unit features an iPad style tablet. The aim is to keep users connected with the outside world and keep them actively conversing. The ability of this machine to interact so effectively makes it seemingly come to life. This social robot is currently in beta testing in the USA.

The Social Scientists

Professor Tia DeNora, social scientist at Exeter University, has a long academic and research history in the field of music and wellbeing. Her latest published work is a six year interdisciplinary study of community music therapy. This longitudinal project is thought to be the most comprehensive in the field. It examines the use of music at a centre supporting people with mental health challenges. It was a collaboration between Professor Gary Ansdell and renowned music therapy charity Nordoff Robbins. This level of examination provides critical evidence to further strengthen the role of music as a wellbeing tool. DeNora is also currently involved in a project examining the effect of everyday music listening on wellbeing in Norway, and another mental health project in the UK. This work will continue to expand as music's positive role in society and in public health continues to be championed by experts in the field.

I'd like to see a closer alignment in future research between the music used in studies and the actual tastes of the participants. Many researchers are themselves immersed in a classical or jazz based environment due to their own experiences and tastes. So often their research is also based in these genres. However, the mass audience (the general public) is much more closely aligned with popular music tastes than with classical or jazz. These taste preferences need to be recognised so that the results can be maximised. For example, children who are taught to play a classical instrument through a classical repertoire setting do experience cognitive benefits. But how much greater might those benefits be if the music used was the music they loved in their every day lives. Sport scientists use pre-screening tools to ascertain the music that is likely to best engage the participants and produce the greatest results. This doesn't seem to happen in other music fields. These studies don't seem to go into depth regarding how and why the music used in the studies was chosen.

I heard a great analogy recently when chatting with the CEO of Young Voices, Ben Lewis. He said "children enthusiastically watch football on television at home and then get to play that exact sport in school, whereas they enthusiastically listen to (and watch) music at home and then the music they experience in school is nothing like it because the curriculum is still too classical based". These are the same comments that the participants in my PhD thesis made. Why have education decision makers not corrected this problem over several decades? It's time to catch up with real life.

9. COME TOGETHER

*Joining the dots to experience the full 360°
value of music in our society*

I believe we're on the cusp of a great revival in terms of how we value music in our society. In previous chapters we looked at how the great Greek philosophers Socrates, Plato and Aristotle amongst others heralded music as an asset of immense value for education and health. Their views were held in great esteem and still are. Yet today when experts present these same views (now actually backed up by a huge body of scientific data rather than just anecdotal evidence and general opinion) decision makers don't seem to respect them or take them into account when forming policies for education, health or economic development.

Music venues and street performers in cities and towns have in recent years become classified as "noise", GPs are still more likely to prescribe the pills that the drug companies pitch to them than to send patients to join a local choir or frequent a music venue, international athletes are trained to use music to control anxiety in high stress situations but our military and police forces are not, music isn't currently considered an essential element in the rating of care homes, and the government believes that STEM subjects (science, technology, engineering, mathematics) must take priority over all other learning. It just doesn't make sense. We are ignoring the scientific facts and dismally failing to tap into the valuable results that music can deliver to the human race.

Firstly, I think that popular music has become a victim of its own success. It's not taken as seriously as its highbrow genre cousins classical, opera and jazz. Often this is purely because the decision makers themselves are actually the highbrow audience. Popular music, or "commercial music" as it's often called, is considered by many to be an industry awash with cash and light in cultural content. These views could not be further from the truth. Local grassroots music venues around the world have always had a hand to mouth existence. You don't make money from unknown acts. This is why these small venues are often run by passionate music fans who get their kicks by helping emerging artists hone their live skills on their stage. The commercial music industry is not awash with cash apart from the privileged few at the top – just like any other sector. It's also not light in cultural content. The V&A museum and London Museum and several other museums around the world have featured popular music themed exhibitions in the past few years and this programming is likely to increase. Popular music subcultures are rich in cultural content and narrate the social issues that were rampant at the time of the birth of these music subgenres. They also have large lifelong audiences.

Secondly, I think we now live in a world where it is increasingly difficult for facts to be heard. Especially when you need to be heard by decision makers. There is plenty of published scientific evidence that backs up all these facts and UK Parliament has itself run several commissions and All Party Parliamentary Groups about specific music related topics such as its role in dementia or education or general wellbeing. But these reports fade into the distance and don't seem to be resulting in changes in policy at a government level. This is what's needed. In fact the only real breakthrough I've witnessed in the past few years is the lobbying campaign to protect grassroots music venues, driven passionately by the Music Venue Trust and supported by The Mayor of London and the Greater London Authority. This did result in a change in planning policy to give much greater protection to small music venues in the UK. The 'Agent of Change Principle' is now written into the National Planning Policy Framework specifying that any property developer wanting to build residential property near an existing music venue is responsible for ensuring there is adequate sound proofing in place. This principle has also been in place in Australia since 2014. Hopefully other countries will quickly follow.

Recently, the music industry publication, *IQ Magazine*,

published my article titled "The 360° Value of Live Music To Society". This topic has become my obsession. I'm on a mission to help join the dots so we stop measuring music in silos and start harnessing its complete power as a tool to drive economic prosperity and improved public health across all age groups, income levels and ethnic backgrounds. Since its publication I have received a number of messages about this article from people I've never met. It seems to have struck a chord. Good. It's time for everyone to come together in a joined up conversation so that we can start properly harnessing music to deliver a multitude of benefits throughout life.

Let's figure out as soon as possible - before all the music venues have closed and all the musicians have moved away - how to help people get more music in their daily lives in every community. This needs to happen at all ages, from providing music sessions for soon-to-be parents in Mothercare stores, to embedding music plans in all care homes as part of later life care. All this knowledge already exists. We know that music is critical in our human development, even before we're born.

We know that it can help us focus to achieve goals. We know that it can help people improve their general health at all ages. We know that it can help combat loneliness and the symptoms of many neurological conditions and improve quality of life. We know that it is a universal language that, whatever your age, race, religion or size of bank balance, your brain processes in the same way.

So with all of this knowledge gathered over many decades

why the heck is music (popular music in particular) constantly "under threat" these days. It's at risk of disappearing from schools, it's only present in 5% of UK care homes (as reported by The Utley Foundation's music and dementia commission), it's being banished (or restricted) from our streets, it's struggling to secure public funding from arts bodies, and it's non-existent in workforce wellbeing programmes.

I like to compare popular music with diamonds. The word diamond stems from the Greek word adamas which means invincible. This perfectly represents a true rock and roll "f#*# you" attitude. The raw stones are not particularly impressive in their rough form before they are cut and polished, but those who possess the knowledge to recognise their value reap the rewards big time. Those who do not recognise their potential value consider them just ordinary stones. They pass over these gems and miss out. We need to teach the decision makers how to recognise rough diamonds and polish them up into highly effective policies. This really hit home recently when I met a new CEO at a local authority. He said he really wanted to understand how music could make an impact but at present had no idea how music could deliver the public health and economic results I was presenting. This was a good reminder. To me these facts are obvious because I'm immersed in this field on an hourly basis, and have been for over 20 years. But for others it's not so obvious. They don't see music as an asset. So it's really important that we manage to convey these facts in a simple enough manner that everyone can very quickly understand the opportunity that's at our fingertips and grasp hold of it. I hope this book will go some way to achieving that knowledge transfer.

There was a media frenzy in the UK recently when UK Music CEO and former UK Member of Parliament, Michael Dugher, published an article announcing that the Arts Council funding policy for music was deeply flawed and unfair. The Arts Council has the responsibility of distributing a significant amount of public funding. UK Music's analysis of the Arts Council funding in 2018 found that popular music will receive just 8% of the £368 million allocated to music over the next four years. Meanwhile a whopping 85% of that £368 million funding pot will be given to opera and classical music. Dugher warned that the Arts Council is appearing elitist and "too posh for pop". I think this argument is one that needs to be pushed to the next level. In order to get the most value from music we need to give people what they want. We need to match their tastes. This drives much more engagement and that in turn will deliver enhanced results in terms of social inclusion and wellbeing. The Arts Council mission statement lists 5 goals: excellence; for everyone; resilience and sustainability; diversity and skills; children and young people. This funding strategy is completely and utterly flawed if popular music genres only receive 8% of music funding. It's simply idiotic. And even more so when you consider that one of the Arts Council's goals is to engage children and young people.

Popular music is now more than sixty years old. It has achieved cultural legitimacy – ask the V&A Museum about that. If an Elvis themed festival is more likely to successfully drive audience engagement than a classical concert give them an Elvis festival. If a 1970s themed outdoor disco is more successful than a performance art piece give them an outdoor disco. I think it's time organisations such as the Arts Council stopped giving people what they think they "should" be listening to and instead helped give them more of the art they enjoy and identify with. The Arts Council's remit is to "champion, develop and invest in artistic and cultural experiences that enrich people's lives". The Arts Council's recent report in 2018 stated that people they surveyed had said music had made their lives better more than anything else. Based on the ticket sales for popular music events versus classical, opera and jazz events and my own research findings I feel confident in saying that when they say "music" the majority of those respondents are actually referring to "popular music". The genre that at present shockingly only receives 8% of music funding. I think a serious conversation needs to be had at a government level regarding the definition of "enriching people's lives". Because I can 100% assure you that when you provide a quality popular music experience that matches the taste preferences of communities it significantly enriches peoples' lives on a mass scale. Acknowledge and respect the music they like and help them get more access to it. Music from our youth has a lifelong effect. The success of popular music over the past six decades or more has left an immediate opportunity to use popular music themes to bring people together. Let's stop repeating past mistakes. Popular music culture is artistically valid and can deliver a broad range of benefits to our society if we start properly supporting it and delivering it. It's a gross missed opportunity if we do not.

It's time to take new approaches to health. Experience has shown that our previous approaches haven't worked. Health warnings seem to have fallen on deaf ears amongst the general public. For example, despite banning it, taxing it and educating the public about the immensely harmful effects of cigarettes using some terrifying visual advertising there are still 9 million people who smoke in the UK and 37 million people who still smoke in the USA. They don't want to stop. They know they should but they enjoy it too much. Some want to give up but find it too hard. Smoking is the primary cause of preventable illness and deaths in the UK and USA. Now Public Health England, the NHS, the British Medical Association and Cancer UK have agreed that if all else fails getting smokers to just switch from cigarettes to vaping is the next best thing. No-one yet knows the long term effects of vaping of course but at least in the short term it can have a beneficial effect. Switching to vaping is far more likely to happen than giving up smoking altogether.

People are more likely to engage in things they enjoy. They are far more likely to put more music engagement and social activity in their lives than they are to exercise more regularly. Because it's more enjoyable. A diet of daily music through listening, singing, dancing, performing, creating or exercising will produce results. Music is already omnipresent. It's an integral part of society and all around us. But if we start paying attention to its power and help harness it in a more structured way I believe the results would be astounding. It would be a gamechanger. We are already living in a musical landscape, especially now that music is so easily accessible through streaming services. Mainstream pop music is particularly influential in defining society. It's played a significant role in driving collective identity and communicating political stances. Since the rise of the teenager in the 1950s, pop music has shaped our cultures and identities and left a lifelong imprint.

In recent years it's true to say that I've become rather obsessed (although I prefer to describe it as passionate) with driving home these messages regarding the health and wellbeing value of recorded music and live performance. This is largely due to the slightly unusual career path that I've travelled. From an early start in the world of exercise and sport psychology with Olympic squads to now consulting on projects such as the creation of the Mayor of London's street performance taskforce to stop busking from being wiped off public streets. I sit on the London Music Board to support the work of the Greater London Authority and Music Venue Trust in protecting grassroots venues. I provide evidence for the Music & Dementia Commission at the House of Lords. I provide evidence regarding the value of music in schools as a Trustee of Young Voices Concerts Foundation. I participate in the All Party Parliamentary Group for Artificial Intelligence to remind everyone of the value of music and art education alongside STEM subjects. There seems to be an endless number of campaigns, committees, boards, and commissions these days that are all examining the value of music and trying to remove the pressures that have been put on it in recent years. It's great that this is all happening and that there is energy around these campaigns. However, due to the fact that I'm fortunate enough to be involved in many of them I'm realizing that the true value of music is actually being completely missed. Because the true value of music to society is when you add them all together into one 360^0 super value.

Music (live music in particular) has unique properties that, when harnessed properly, can drive economic development and improve health and wellbeing (in exceptional ways). There are not many other tools that have such a diverse range of benefits. We have also now entered an era where it's possible to engage multiple generations with popular music. The grandparents invented it and the grandchildren are still devouring it. This has opened new and exciting opportunities for intergenerational line-ups and audiences at concerts and festivals. The perfect driver for socialising lots of age groups together. This phenomenon is only going to grow stronger in the next two decades as the youth of the 1970s/80s/90s become pensioners. Music tastes from youth last a lifetime. For the live industry this offers extensive audiences in the coming years, and large commercial returns. For local authorities and governments this offers opportunities to improve social cohesion in communities, promote their destination to tourists, and to improve public health and economic development.

For this 360° super value to be properly exploited it's essential to bring all of the stakeholders around the same table. Decision makers from the music industry PLUS the urban planners, the education system, the health boards, the economic development and licensing teams all need to talk with each other about these facts. Collaboration and cooperation and the sharing of intelligence and goals will help more music reach more people. In local grassroots venues, in public places, in stadiums, in fields, in stately homes, in castles, in churches, in schools, in workplaces and in care homes. As the value of music becomes more and more recognised I hope red tape will continue to be removed (or adjusted) in order to support and facilitate more music opportunities. Strategies will eventually, I hope, become more aligned and will feed into each other.

All the previous chapters in this book have championed how attending live music events, learning to play musical instruments, singing, dancing, listening to and creating music has a portfolio of benefits – for the economy and for health. The scientific evidence base regarding these facts is now so large it's undeniable. Music is an essential part of human life. It's in our DNA. It provides many magical benefits from the womb to the grave.

I've made it my mission to urge cities, towns, governments, organisations, property developers and businesses from all sectors to bring all the stakeholders together into one joined up conversation. Let's stop using a silo approach and instead measure the true value of music across **all** aspects of society. Then we can work together to make plans that ensure that we get as much music into as many people's lives as possible. Music makes life better. It's a fact. Music can increase happiness (this is scientifically proven and driven by automatic neurochemical reactions) especially when experienced in social environments. Happiness is key to wellbeing. People buy and eagerly consume things that make them happy. The live music industry and popular music culture has a significant contribution to make in this regard.

Over the past 2 years I've been immersed in these conversations. I want to help ensure that 2019 is the 'eureka' year. When everyone finally joins one single conversation and really starts to harness the full 360° super value of music.

HOW DO I APPLY THIS IN LIFE?

In Local Government and National Government

We need to encourage decision makers to start thinking how they can work more closely to achieve these results in your community. The decision makers hold the key to success. We need government departments to share information with each other so they can better use that intelligence to drive effective decisions and policies. We need them to connect the dots and see music as a 360° tool rather than just continually considering it in isolation in education, or in health or in public spaces. We need decision makers to adopt the same approach and consider how they can each play a role in this goal. Think how your work can help get more music into the daily lives of more people.

As a CEO of a local authority make sure you put a comprehensive music policy in place. A formal plan that clearly communicates to all your teams how music will be harnessed and supported across a range of outputs from public health to placemaking and tourism marketing.

As a decision maker in education you could ensure that when young teachers are being trained they are fully taught the scientific principles behind the "musician's advantage" so they understand why it's important for children to get as much music exposure and learning during youth as possible. You could ensure that music is protected within the school curriculum so that we produce a new generation workforce that has the soft skills that technology leaders say are currently in short supply within the new fields of Artificial Intelligence and machine learning.

As a decision maker in health you could ensure that expectant parents are taught the value of music exposure in brain development so they fill their home with music engagement during pregnancy and in early pre-school years. You could ensure that the scientific facts relating to the ways in which music automatically delivers positive cognitive and physical effects is taught to all medical students so that the next generation of GPs are more likely to refer a patient (where appropriate) to the local choir or music venue than to prescribe drugs. You could ensure that the official CQC ratings system for care homes fully considers their use of music in enhancing the quality of life of residents.

As a decision maker in arts funding make sure that popular

music culture has the financial capacity to increase its grassroots activity to reach more people in communities. This is the genre that will successfully engage youth audiences as well as older demographics.

As a property developer think about how the designs of your new buildings and towns can be embedded with music opportunities, bringing life to public spaces in and around your development, driving social engagement and happiness and wellbeing.

Early in 2018 I proposed an idea to Lord Tim Clement-Jones, a member of the House of Lords. I wanted to organise a series of "Music in Society" evidence sessions to be held at the House of Lords in late 2018 and early 2019. The aim was to bring everyone together and properly examine music's current and potential future value in the UK. He agreed with this approach. So these sessions will, for the first time, bring evidence from all the different fields into one single conversation featuring a range of experts. Taking the excellent work of various previous Parliamentary APPGs examining related topics and joining them into one single coherent examination. From this approach we can produce one cumulative publication and a best practice model that can hopefully serve as a foundation for achieving a more successful approach in the UK. A series of achievable actions that deliver the maximum impact and return on investment.

We can start to measure the full 360 degree value of music in society by adding together its effect on dementia care, on educational development, on mental health, on crime, on economic development, on social isolation and loneliness, on tourism, on general health and so on. A new approach with ground-breaking shifts in strategy to address and avert the well documented public health crisis and its associated economic repercussions. Governments often move slowly. Patience and persistence is required. Hopefully this book has helped you to begin considering the role that music can play in the rest of your own life so that you can get a head start and rock on while we wait for Parliament to catch up. ☺

The value of music is more than just entertainment. It's the cumulative value of many, many variables. I've been working on a valuation formula since 2015 when I completed my PhD. The current version of this is below but this is still very much a work in progress as I continue to examine how some of these variables can be valued with data analyses that can be used as solid evidence.

Traditionally the value of music has been measured in economic terms based solely on the income derived from core industry revenue streams such as record sales, publishing and live performances. This value, expressed as GVA, is in truth only a fraction of the full value that music delivers to our society. If music as an asset is harnessed effectively it can deliver dramatic returns. Human brains are designed to respond to music even when we are only passively engaging with it. This makes it an extremely effective tool in terms of positively influencing human behaviour. The formula I've set out below aims to give a more comprehensive representation of the full value of music to society. There is a growing body of research relating to each of these variables. It's time to recognise the importance of music as an asset and start extracting its full potential in a strategic and organised manner.

Music Valuation Formula: $VM = (MIr) + (CsH) + (Eg)$

Whereby:
$MIr = (GVA + NCr + MTs)$
$CsH = (Lr + Dp + Dc + Sr + Pc + Wi + Ac + CRi + Ri + Ac + Si)$
$Eg = (WWp + CRr + SWg + Pr)$

Key:

VM - The value of music in modern society

MIr – *Music Industry Revenues:*
GVA – Gross Value Added (core revenues such as record sales, publishing, live ticketing, synchronisation fees: *£4.4bn as measured by UK Music in 2017)*
NCr – Non core revenues (such as instrument sales, studio hire, tuition etc)
MTs – Music Tourism (secondary spends on F&B, retail, travel, accommodation driven specifically by live music events or music heritage)

CsH - *Cost Savings in Health:*
      Lr - Loneliness Reduction
      Dp - Dementia Prevention
      Dc - Dementia Care
      Sr - Stroke Recovery
      Pc - Parkinson's Care

Wi - Wellbeing improvement (physical/mental)

Ac - Autism Care

CRi - Cardio/Respiratory Improvement

Ri - Recovery Improvement

Ac - Anxiety control

Si - Sleep improvement

Eg - *Economic Growth:*

WWp - Workforce Wellbeing/Productivity

CRr - Crime and Re-Offending Reduction

SWg - Skilled Workforce Growth

Pr - Placemaking Revenue

The world is certainly waking up to the full potential of music. It's much more than mere entertainment. I hope this book has helped inspire you to get as much music in your life and business as you can.

APPENDIX A

CARE IN LATER LIFE (UK)

How to embed music in local care homes to maintain quality of life

The Care Quality Commission (CQC) in England monitors, inspects and regulates care homes' services. In assessing the quality of services the CQC asks 5 questions. The information below outlines how music can contribute to the outcomes of these assessments as care homes strive to achieve an Outstanding rating (the best of 4 levels: Outstanding, Good, Requires Improvement, Inadequate. The full details of this working paper can be found on the website www.achoirineverycarehome.com

CQC Assessment Question 1
Are they safe?
(By safe we mean that people are protected from abuse and avoidable harm)

Music activities can support social bonding, build relationships and respect, encouraging person-centred care, leading to a safer environment. This is demonstrated by an Evidence Review showing care homes reported fewer accidents and improved sleeping patterns.

CQC Assessment Question 2
Are they affective?
(By effective we mean that people's care, treatment and support achieves good outcomes, promotes a good quality of life and is based upon the best evidence available)

Music activities can contribute to meaningful lives of people living in care. Taking part in music activities develops skills in staff that contribute to how they are equipped to offer holistic and person-centred care. This is demonstrated by an Evidence Review showing families reported that older people were happier as a result of music projects.

CQC Assessment Question 3
Are they caring?
(By caring we mean that services involve and treat people with compassion, kindness, dignity and respect)

Participatory music activities can support bonding, build relationships and respect, encouraging person centred care. Music can support residents to communicate about themselves and their histories. It can improve mood, help with depression and alleviate distress. This is demonstrated through feedback and surveys whereby care homes reported that staff were happier in general and more engaged with residents.

CQC Assessment Question 4
Are they responsive to people's needs?
(By responsive, we mean that services meet people's needs).

Taking part in music can offer residents choices, agency and control. Music is a social communal activity that is open to all. Music can bring people in from outside and connect residents with the wider community. This is demonstrated by feedback and surveys whereby families reported that older people were happier and more engaged with others and in their circumstances during and after music activities.

CQC Assessment Question 5
Are they well-led?
(By well-led, we mean that the leadership, management and governance of the organisation assures the delivery of high-quality person-centred care, supports learning and innovation, and promotes an open and fair culture)

Music can create an open culture and shows spark and innovation. Taking part in music can be empowering and allow people to find new things about themselves and grow creatively. This is demonstrated by feedback and surveys whereby families reported that older people were happier and more engaged, and care homes reported that staff were more motivated and communicative.

Example of Best Practice

(These examples were compiled by Dr Julia Jones and Nina Clark of Musical Walkabout CIC)

TASK AREA	INTERVENTION
Atmospheric	**RECREATIONAL AREAS** Music is played in Reception and recreational areas, setting a welcoming atmosphere for all.

Atmospheric	**<u>SENSORY ENVIRONMENTS</u>** Soothing music is selected for the Sensory Assisted Bathrooms, accompanying the ambient lighting and featured murals.
Research / Administrative	**PERSONAL MUSIC PROFILE** Creation of a musical profile for each resident. Charts their preferences and different musical involvements inside and out of the care setting, including any instrument they might play. Consult resident and family.
Preparation / Family Involvement	**PERSONAL MUSIC COLLECTION** Where possible, encourage residents to bring a selection of their home music collection in when they move in. Liaise with family to facilitate.
Administrative	**<u>DISPLAY PREFERENCES</u>** Add musical preferences to personal 'likes/dislikes' displayed at door to resident room, in bold/different colour to make visible to staff, and visiting family and friends.
Practical Project	**<u>HOME MUSIC LIBRARY</u>** Gather selection of vinyl / CDs. This may comprise of personal contributions from residents, family, friends or staff, or purchased at low cost from charity shops.
Research Maintenance	**<u>PASSIVE ACCESS TO MUSIC</u>** Radios in rooms. Utilise resident preferences/choices when selecting

	channels.
Purchases	**ACTIVE ACCESS TO MUSIC** CD players in rooms. Encourage family to purchase (average cost £20), use resident's own musical collection, or from the Home Music Library.
Purchases / Project / Group or 1-2-1 Activity	**VINYL CORNER** An area where residents can play (their) records. Small portable record players with integral speakers retail at around £30, allowing the experience to reach room-bound residents.
Group or 1-2-1 Activity	**MUSIC AND MEMORIES** Interactive session using music to prompt reminiscence, communication (Vinyl Corner could expand into this)
Group Activity	**THEMED MUSIC EVENTS** Staff Musicals/Pantos, King Elvises and Graceland link-up, talent shows- involving residents in events that connect them with the wider world / a specific genre / idea. Creating interactive events is best practice.
Group Access Environment	**PUBLIC HOUSE** The new on-site pub has plans to host musical artists and karaoke sessions. Further possibilities include music quizzes and open mics.
Group Activity	**WORSHIP** The home has a weekly communion

	service held in the second floor lounge, where singing hymns is a feature of the observance.
Group Activity/ Research	**MUSICAL ENTERTAINMENT** Weekly visit from a musical entertainer. The home has a wide roster of artists that rotate throughout the year. Staff research has flagged up need for entertainers to play a more varied/modern repertoire to cater to younger residents.
Group Activity / External	**WORKSHOPS** Drumming / percussion workshops / activities. Has been shown to help clients appropriately vent frustration, and operate as an alternative method of communicating. Could be led by a professional music therapist, or after training with such a practitioner, could be adapted to a percussive play-along led by staff using pre-existing music.
Group Activity / External	**SINGING** The in-house choir (scheduled weekly) has members from the wider community, encouraging community cohesion, and has performed at public engagements around Kent, as well as recording their own album of songs.
Group Activity	**MUSIC FOR HEALTH** Group music workshops covering a range of themes - reminiscence / rhythm / engagement. Promotes social inclusion and creative participation within the home and the community of

	residents.
1-2-1 Activity	**MUSIC LESSONS** *"Music keeps your ears young. Older musicians don't experience typical aging in the part of the brain (the auditory cortex) that often leads to hearing troubles. It's never too late to start taking piano lessons and prevent these age-related changes (The Record.com – Michael Roizen, MD and Mehmet Oz, MD)."* The Grand Piano in reception could be utilized for lessons.
1-2-1 / Group Activity	**MUSICAL WALKABOUT** Bespoke minstrelling, person-centred for those more confined to their rooms and socially isolated. Resident preferences are logged, allowing them to curate their own musical engagement. Varied repertoire offers a wide range of options to residents, and songs can be learnt on request.
Staff Group Activity	**LEAGUE OF AMIABLE SONGSTERS** Group singing for staff wellbeing sessions. Based on a feasibility study by Ann Skingley of Sidney De Haan Research Centre for Arts and Health in NHS (WE Care Choir, led by Nina Clark). Distinct from the in-house choir, as specifically for staff rather than residents. There is evidence to show that such interventions are valuable to staff health and wellbeing, therefore positively impacting job performance.

SOURCE MATERIAL

The active hyperlinks for these sources can be accessed at

www.musicdiet.co.uk

https://www.ihrsa.org/about/media-center/press-releases/ihrsa-2018-global-report-club-industry-revenue-totaled-87-2-billion-in-2017

http://www.leisuredb.com/blog/2018/5/16/2018-state-of-the-uk-fitness-industry-report-out-now

https://www.theguardian.com/culture/2009/sep/08/fame-tv-influence

http://www.diabetes.org/diabetes-basics/statistics/

https://www.bmj.com/bmj/section-pdf/186279?path=/bmj/342/7803/Head_to_Head.full.pdf

https://www.britannica.com/topic/physical-culture#ref858769

http://www.euro.who.int/en/health-topics/noncommunicable-diseases/diabetes/data-and-statistics

https://www.gov.uk/government/news/modern-life-responsible-for-worrying-health-in-middle-aged

https://www.theguardian.com/fashion/2017/apr/22/big-guys-fashion-plus-sized-menswear-revolution

http://www.nytimes.com/1983/08/03/garden/self-help-videotapes-from-cooking-to-car-repair.html

http://www.inquisitr.com/1754742/jane-fonda-talks-low-carb-diet-fitness-dvds-and-beauty-tips-to-stay-sexy-at-77-video/

https://www.supertracker.usda.gov/bwp/index.html

http://www.mintel.com/press-centre/retail-press-centre/fashionistas-cause-sales-of-sportswear-to-sprint-uk-sports-goods-sales-estimated-to-surpass-7-billion-in-2016

https://www.sportengland.org/research/who-plays-sport/national-picture/

http://www.pfma.org.uk/pet-population-2016

https://academic.oup.com/jnci/article/doi/10.1093/jnci/dju206/1010488/Sedentary-behavior-increases-the-risk-of-certain

https://www2.deloitte.com/uk/en/pages/press-releases/articles/uk-public-glued-to-smartphones.html

http://www2.le.ac.uk/departments/media/documents/Fit%

20for%20Consumption%20%20Synopsis%20of%20Health
%20Implications.pdfhttps://www.theguardian.com/society/
2016/sep/03/hospitals-to-cut-costs-by-denying-surgery-to-
smokers-and-the-obese

https://www.alzheimers.org.uk/info/20027/news_and_med
ia/541/facts_for_the_media

[14]http://www.standard.co.uk/lifestyle/esmagazine/why-the-
superrich-are-ploughing-billions-into-the-booming-
immortality-industry-a3575416.html

https://www.london.gov.uk/press-releases/mayoral/mayor-
places-culture-at-heart-of-london-plan

http://www.nme.com/list/100-best-songs-of-the-1980s-
1161

https://www.independent.co.uk/news/blair-is-mr-93-
1241567.html

http://www.independent.co.uk/travel/asia/japan-northern-
soul-music-kobe-club-night-nude-restaurant-o-jays-never-
forget-you-gonna-be-a-big-a7990431.html

https://www.theguardian.com/culture/2016/oct/06/desert-
trip-festival-oldchella-coachella-review

http://variety.com/2017/music/news/classic-north-west-
seattle-eagles-doobie-brothers-1202503866/

https://www.theguardian.com/music/2017/dec/22/the-
best-albums-of-2017-no-1-st-vincent-masseduction

http://westminsterresearch.wmin.ac.uk/15359/

Brunel Music Rating Inventory (BMRI: Karageorghis et al., 1999: Journal of Sports Sciences, 17, 713±724).

Karageorghis, C 2000, Journal of Sport Sciences, 18, 12-21 (this is my MSc research project and article but was published in Costas Karageorghis' name alone and excluded my name – an apology was issued in a later publication)

Levitin, D (2007) "This Is Your Brain On Music: The Science of a Human Obsession", Penguin.

https://www.mayfieldclinic.com/PE-AnatBrain.htm

https://www.amazon.co.uk/How-Music-Works-David-Byrne/dp/0857862529

https://www.smithsonianmag.com/arts-culture/how-do-our-brains-process-music-32150302/?page=2

https://daniellevitin.com/levitinlab/articles/2013-TICS_1180.pdf

http://journals.plos.org/plosone/article?id=10.1371/journal.pone.0013225

https://www.amazon.co.uk/Musicophilia-Tales-Music-Oliver-Sacks/dp/0330523597

https://www.ncbi.nlm.nih.gov/pmc/articles/PMC1281386/

https://www.ncbi.nlm.nih.gov/pmc/articles/PMC4269311/

pdf/IJAD2014-836748.pdf

https://www.ncbi.nlm.nih.gov/pmc/articles/PMC2996135/

http://www.diw.de/documents/publikationen/73/diw_01.c.
429221.de/diw_sp0591.pdf

https://www.ncbi.nlm.nih.gov/pubmed/17943015

http://www.brainvolts.northwestern.edu/documents/Tiern
ey_Kraus_Chapter_2014.pdf

http://neurosciencenews.com/early-music-lessons-boost-
brain-development/

http://www.jneurosci.org/content/33/3/1282

https://www.sciencedaily.com/releases/2014/12/141223132
546.htm

https://medicalxpress.com/news/2008-10-musicians-sides-
brains-frequently-average.html

https://blog.bufferapp.com/why-practice-actually-makes-
perfect-how-to-rewire-your-brain-for-better-
performance#footnotes

http://www.brainmusic.org/EducationalActivitiesFolder/B
engtsson_practicing2005.pdf

https://www.rollingstone.com/music/news/flea-removing-
music-education-from-schools-is-child-abuse-w497593

http://www.bbc.co.uk/news/education-39154242

https://musiceducationworks.wordpress.com/2017/10/03/how-a-bradford-primary-school-improved-its-sats-results-with-music/

https://www.theguardian.com/education/2016/oct/24/want-to-train-your-brain-forget-apps-learn-a-musical-instrument

https://mic.com/articles/110628/13-scientific-studies-prove-music-lessons-were-the-best-thing-your-parents-did-for-you#.gDy5LVe89

https://draxe.com/sarcopenia/

https://www.keckmedicine.org/can-brain-activity-and-exercise-delay-alzheimers-disease/

https://news.nationalgeographic.com/news/2014/01/140103-music-lessons-brain-aging-cognitive-neuroscience/

https://greatergood.berkeley.edu/article/item/science_of_singing

https://nos.org.uk/

https://www.nice.org.uk/guidance/cg146/chapter/introduction

https://www.newscientist.com/article/mg22730335-000-why-music-makes-us-feel-good-it-releases-brains-painkillers/

https://nos.org.uk/news/2017/december/21/shall-we-dance-dance-yourself-to-better-bone-health/

http://time.com/4828793/dancing-dance-aerobic-exercise/

http://www.huffingtonpost.co.uk/entry/how-music-affects-workout_us_55d746a3e4b0a40aa3aaa9da#gallery/55d7484
9e4b08cd3359bd104/5

http://www.who.int/ageing/global-strategy/en/

http://www.ilcuk.org.uk/index.php/news/news_posts/press
_release_older_people_spending_more_time_in_ill_health
_as_health_inequ

https://www.campaigntoendloneliness.org/loneliness-research/

https://www.campaigntoendloneliness.org/wp-content/uploads/Tackling-Loneliness-A-Role-for-the-Arts1.pdf

http://nua.unhabitat.org/uploads/WCRFullReport2016_E
N.pdf

https://historicengland.org.uk/listing/the-list/list-entry/1427422

http://www.bbc.co.uk/news/uk-england-38609692

https://global.oup.com/academic/product/going-to-the-palais-9780199605194?cc=gb&lang=en&

http://www.bbc.co.uk/news/uk-england-38609692

http://musicvenuetrust.com/wp-content/uploads/2015/02/rescue_plan_for_londons_grassr

oots_music_venues_-_progress_update_-_jan_2017.pdf

http://musicvenuetrust.com/2017/11/agent-of-change-is-policy-d12-in-london-plan-2018/

http://www.press.uchicago.edu/pressReleases/2013/July/729Pieters.html

https://www.ncbi.nlm.nih.gov/pmc/articles/PMC3406601/

https://www.livescience.com/18800-loneliness-health-problems.html

https://www.eurekalert.org/pub_releases/2015-01/ica-fol012615.php

https://www.nationwide.co.uk/about/media-centre-and-specialist-areas/media-centre/press-releases/archive/2017/3/02-fraudsters

https://www.gov.uk/government/uploads/system/uploads/attachment_data/file/262139/Dementia.pdf

https://www.alzheimers.org.uk/download/downloads/id/2323/dementia_uk_update.pdf

https://jamanetwork.com/journals/jamainternalmedicine/fullarticle/2587084

https://www.alz.org/facts/

http://www.who.int/features/factfiles/dementia/en/

http://baringfoundation.org.uk/wp-content/uploads/2015/05/GettingOn.pdf

https://achoirineverycarehome.files.wordpress.com/2016/0
4/wp4-trends-in-the-care-home-sector.pdf

http://www.ilcuk.org.uk/index.php/publications/publicatio
n_details/what_would_life_be_without_a_song_or_dance_
what_are_we

https://www.parkinsons.org.uk/about-us/media-and-press-
office

https://www.ncbi.nlm.nih.gov/pmc/articles/PMC4553388/

https://singforjoychoirs.org.uk/portfolio/our-history/

http://newsfeed.time.com/2012/04/11/alzheimers-patient-
awakens-when-listening-to-music-from-his-past/

https://www.thelancet.com/journals/lancet/article/PIIS014
0-6736(17)30398-7/abstract?code=lancet-site

https://news.usc.edu/131274/music-training-can-change-
childrens-brain-structure-and-boost-decision-making-
network/

https://neurosciencenews.com/music-chills-neuroscience-
6167/

https://www.brainvolts.northwestern.edu/documents/Krau
s_White-Schwoch_Neuroscientist2017.pdf

https://edition-m.cnn.com/2018/08/06/europe/germany-elderly-heavy-metal-rockers-intl/index.html

http://journals.plos.org/plosone/article?id=10.1371/journal
.pone.0193819

ABOUT THE AUTHOR

(Photo: Julia Jones and Jane Fonda, London 2017)

Julia Jones was born in Pembrokeshire, Wales in 1970. She now lives in Folkestone on the south coast of England. She started collecting records and DJing in the 1970s, taught herself to play guitar and joined her first band in the 1980s. She recorded and self-released her first album of her own songs in New York City in 2003.

Julia gained a BA (Hons) and MSc in Sport and Exercise Science in the 1990s. Her MBA and PhD theses both examined the effect of music on human behaviour and business. Her research has been published in scientific and trade journals and featured on radio and television. She advises public and private sector clients, prescribing music to achieve economic, social and wellbeing goals.

The following blank pages are for your notes. As you work your way through these chapters and think "Yes! I'd like to do that!" write these eureka moments down here. Then rip these pages out and stick them at eye level on your fridge door! Or set some reminders on your smartphone if you no longer own a pen. Good luck!

THE MUSIC DIET

THE MUSIC DIET

THE MUSIC DIET